O. HENRY

AMONG THE HUMORISTS AND AFTER-DINNER SPEAKERS

A NEW COLLECTION OF HUMOROUS STORIES AND ANECDOTES

SELECTED AND ARRANGED BY

WILLIAM PATTEN

Editor of American Short Story Classics,
Foreign Short Story Classics, etc.

VOL. III

P. F. COLLIER & SON
NEW YORK

CONTENTS—VOLUME III

THE SEER AND THE SERVANT

BY JOSEPH C. LINCOLN

"YUP," says Effie, bobbin' her head so emphatic that the sky-blue ribbon pennants on her black hair flapped like a loose tops'l in a gale of wind. "Yup," says she, "I b'lieve it just as much as I b'lieve anything. How could I help it when he told me so much that has come true already? He said I'd seen trouble, and the dear land knows that's so! and that I might see more, and I cal'late that's pretty average likely. And he said I hadn't been brought up in luxury—"

"Which wa'n't no exaggeration neither," I put in, thinkin' of the shack over on the Neck Road where she and her folks used to live.

"No," says she; "and he told me I'd always had longin's for better and higher things and that my intellectuals was above my station. Well, ever since I was knee high to a kitchen chair I'd ruther work upstairs than down, and as for intellectuals, Ma always said I was the smartest young one she'd raised yet. So them statements give me consider'ble confidence. But he give out that I was to make a journey and get money, and when *that* come true I held up both hands and stood ready to swaller all the rest of it."

"So it come true, did it?" says I.

"Um-hm," says she, bouncin' her head again. "Inside of four year I traveled 'way over to South Eastboro—'most twelve mile—to my Uncle Izzy's fun'ral, and there I found that he'd left me nine hundred dollars for my very own. And down I flops on the parlor sofy and says I: 'There! don't talk superstition to *me* no more! A person that can foretell Uncle Izzy's givin' anybody a cent, let alone nine hundred dollars, is a good enough prophet for *me* to tie to. Now I *know* that I'm going to marry the dark-complected man, and I'll be ready for him when he comes along. I never spent a quarter no better than when I handed it over to that Oriental Seer critter at the cattle show.' That's what I said then and I b'lieve it yet. Wouldn't you feel the same way?"

I said sure thing I would. I'd found out that the best way to keep Effie's talk-shop runnin' was to agree with her. And I liked to hear her talk. She was third assistant roustabout and table girl at the Old Home House the fourth season that me and Cap'n Jonadab and Peter T. Brown run it. She'd never worked out afore and was greener than a mess of spinach; but she was kind of pretty to look at and I'd sort of took a fancy to her. I never did have the high-toned ideas about not bein' familiar with help that Jonadab suffered from. 'Twan't so many years since I was fo'mast hand myself.

So Effie'd got in the habit of tellin' me all her troubles and secrets. Just now she was unloadin' some more or less facts concernin' what a specimen who cruised under the name of "The Marvelous Oriental Seer" had handed in change for a quarter at the Ostable County cattle show and fair.

"Yup," she went on, "I give right in then. I'd traveled same as the fortune teller said, and I'd got more money 'n I ever expected to see, let alone own. And ever sence I've been sartin as I'm alive that the feller I marry will be of a rank higher'n mine and dark complected and good-lookin' and distinguished, and that he'll be name of Butler."

"Butler?" says I. "What will he be named Butler for?"

" 'Cause the Seer critter said so. He said he could see the word Butler printed out over the top of my head in flamin' letters. Pa used to say 'twas a wonder it never set fire to my crimps, but he was only foolin'. *I* know that it's all comin' out true. You ain't acquaintanced to any Butlers, are you?"

"No," says I. "I heard Ben Butler make a speech once when he was gov'nor, but he's dead now. There ain't no Butlers on the Old Home shippin' lists."

"Oh, I know that!" she says. "And everybody round here is homelier'n a moultin' pullet. There now! I didn't mean exactly *everybody,* of course. But you ain't dark-complected, you know, nor—"

"No," says I, "nor rank nor distinguished neither. 'Course the handsome part might fit me, but I'd have to pass on the rest of the hand. That's all right, Effie; my feelin's have got fireproofed since I've been in the summer hotel business. Now you'd better run along and report to Susannah. I hear her whoopin' for you, and she don't light like a canary bird on the party she's mad with."

She didn't, that was a fact. Susannah Debs, who was housekeeper for us that year, was middlin' young and middlin' good-lookin', and couldn't forget it.

Also and likewise, she had a suit for damages against the railroad, which she had hopes would fetch her money some day or other, and she couldn't forget that neither. She was skipper of all the hired hands and, bein' as Effie was prettier than she was, never lost a chance to lay the poor girl out. She put the other help up to pokin' fun at Effie's green ways and high-toned notions, and 'twas her that started 'em callin' her "Lady Evelyn" in the fo'castle—servants' quarters, I mean.

"I'm a-comin'," screams Effie, startin' for the door. "Susannah's in a tearin' hurry to get through early to-day," she adds to me. "She's got the afternoon off and her beau's comin' to take her buggy-ridin'. He's from over Harniss way somewheres, and they say he's just lovely. My sakes! I wisht sombody'd take me to ride. Ah hum! cal'late I'll have to wait for my Butler man. Say, Mr. Wingate, you won't mention my fortune to a soul, will you? I've never told anybody but you."

I promised to keep mum, and she cleared out. After dinner, as I was smokin', along with Cap'n Jonadab, on the side piazza, a horse and buggy drove in at the back gate. A young chap with black curly hair was pilotin' the craft. He was a stranger to me, wore a checkerboard suit and a bonfire necktie, and had his hat twisted over one ear. Altogether he looked some like a sunflower goin' to seed.

"Who's that barber's sign when it's to home?" says I to Jonadab. He snorted contemptuous.

"That?" he says. "Don't you know the cut of that critter's jib? He plays pool, for just a home, in Web Saunders's place over to Orham. He's the housekeeper's steady comp'ny—steady by spells, if all I hear's true. Good-for-nothin' cub, I call him. Wisht I'd had him aboard a vessel of mine; I'd 'a' squared his yards for him. Look how he cants his hat to starboard so's to show them lovelocks. Bah!"

"What's his name?" I asks.

"Name? Name's Butler—Simeon Butler. Don't you remember . . . Hey? What in tunket . . . ?"

Both of us had jumped as if somebody'd touched off a bombshell under our main hatches. The windows of the dining-room was right astern of us. We whirled round, and there was Effie. She'd been clearin' off one of the tables, and there she stood, with the smashed pieces of an ice-cream platter in front of her, the melted cream sloppin' over her shoes, and her face lookin' like the picture of Lot's wife just turnin' to salt. Only Effie looked as if she enjoyed the turnin'. She never spoke nor moved, just stared after that buggy, with her black eyes sparklin' like burnt holes in a blanket.

I was too astonished to say anything, but Jonadab had his eye on that smashed platter, and *he* had things to say, plenty of 'em. I walked off and left Effie playin' congregation to a sermon on the text, "Crockery costs money." You'd think that ice-cream dish was a genuine, ugly, nicked "antique" wuth any city loon's ten dollars, instead of bein' only new and pretty fifty-cent china. I felt real sorry for the poor girl.

But I needn't have been. That evenin' I found her on the back steps, all Sunday duds and airs. Her hair had a wire friz on it, and her dress had Joseph's coat in Scriptur' lookin' like a mournin' rig. She'd have been real handsome—to a body that was color blind.

"My, Effie!" says I, "you sartin do look fine to-night."

"Yup," she says, contented, "I guess likely I do. Hope so, 'cause I'm wearin' all I've got. Say, Mr. Wingate," says she, excited as a cat in a fit, "did you see him?"

"Him?" says I. "Who's him?"

"Why, *him!* The one the Seer said was comin'. The handsome, dark-complected feller I'm goin' to marry. The Butler one. That was him in the buggy this afternoon."

I looked at her. I'd forgot all about the fool prophecy.

"Good land of love!" I says. "You don't cal'late he's comin' to marry *you,* do you, just 'cause his name's Butler? There's ten thousand Butlers in the world. Besides, your particular one was slated to be high ranked and distinguished, and this specimen scrubs up the billiard-room floor and ain't no more distinguished than a poor-house pig."

"Ain't?" she sings out. "Ain't distinguished? With all them beautiful curls, and rings on his fingers, and—?"

"Bells on his toes? No!" says I, emphatic. "Anyhow, he's signed for the v'yage already. He's Susannah Debs's steady, and they're off buggy-ridin' together right now. And if she catches you makin' eyes at her best feller—Whew!"

Didn't make no difference. He was her Butler, sure. 'Twas Fate—that's what 'twas—Fate, just the same as in story books. She was sorry for poor Susannah and she wouldn't do nothin' mean nor underhanded; but couldn't I understand that 'twas all planned out for her by Providence and that everlastin' Seer? Just let me watch and see, that's all.

What can you do with an idiot like that? I walked off disgusted and left her. But I cal'lated to watch. I judged 'twould be more fun than any play-actin' show ever *I* took in.

And 'twas, in a way. Don't ask me how they got acquainted, 'cause I can't tell you for sartin. Nigh's I can learn, Susannah and Sim had some sort of lover's row durin' their buggy ride, and when they got back to the hotel they was scurcely on speakin' terms. And Sim, who always had a watch out for'ard for pretty girls, see Effie standin' on the servants' porch all togged up regardless and gay as a tea-store chromo, and nothin' to do but he must be introduced. One of the stable hands done the introducin', I b'lieve, and if he'd have been hung afterwards 'twould have sarved him right.

Anyhow, inside of a week Butler come round again to take a lady friend drivin', but this time 'twas Effie, not the housekeeper, that was passenger. And Susannah glared after 'em like a cat after a sparrow, and the very next day she was for havin' Effie discharged for incompetentiveness. I give Jonadab the tip, though, so that didn't go through. But I cal'late there was a parrot and monkey time amongst the help from then on. They all sided with Susannah, of course. She was their boss, for one thing, and "Lady Evelyn's" high-minded notions wa'n't popular, for another. But Effie didn't care—bless you, no! She and that Butler sport was together more and more, and the next thing I heard was they was engaged. I snum if it didn't look as if the Oriental man knew his job, after all.

I spoke to the stable hand about it.

" Look here," says I, " is this business betwixt that pool player and our Effie serious?"

He laughed. "Serious enough, I guess," he says. "They're goin' to be married pretty soon, I hear. It's all 'cordin' to the law and the prophets. Ain't you heard about the fortune tellin' and how 'twas foretold she'd marry a Butler?"

I'd heard, but I didn't s'pose he had. However, it seemed that Effie hadn't been able to keep it to herself no longer. Soon as she'd hooked her man she'd blabbed the whole thing. The fo'mast hands wa'n't talkin' of nothin' else, so this feller said.

"Humph!" says I. "Is it the prophecy that Butler's bankin' on?"

He laughed again. "Not so much as on Lady Evelyn's nine hundred, I cal'late," says he. "Sim likes Susannah the best of the two, so we all reckon, but she ain't rich and Effie is. And yet, if the Debs woman should win that lawsuit of hers against the railroad she'd have pretty nigh twice as much. Butler's a fool not to wait, *I* think," he says.

This was of a Monday. On Friday evenin' Effie comes around to see me. I was alone in the office.

"Mr. Wingate," she says, "I'm goin' to leave tomorrer night. I'm goin' to be married on Sunday."

I'd been expecting it, but I couldn't help feelin' sorry for her.

"Don't do nothin' rash, Effie," I told her. "Are you sure that Butler critter cares anything about you and not your money?"

She flared up like a tar barrel. "The idea!" she

says, turnin' red. "I just come in to give you warnin'. Good by."

"Hold on," I sung out to her. "Effie, I've thought consider'ble about you lately. I've been tryin' to help you a little on the sly. I realized that 'twa'n't pleasant for you workin' here under Susannah Debs, and I've been tryin' to find a nice place for you. I wrote about you to Bob Van Wedderburn; he's the rich banker chap who stopped here one summer. 'Jonesy,' we used to call him. I know him and his wife fustrate, and he'd do 'most anything as a favor to me. I told him what a neat, handy girl you was, and he writes that he'll give you the job of second girl at his swell New York house, if you want it. Now you just hand that Sam Butler his clearance papers and go work for Bob's wife. The wages are double what you get here, and—"

She didn't wait to hear the rest. Just sailed out of the room with her nose in the air. In a minute, though, back she come and just put her head in the door.

"I'm much obliged to you Mr. Wingate," says she. "I know you mean well. But you ain't had your fate foretold, same's I have. It's all been arranged for me, and I couldn't stop it no more'n Jonah could help swallerin' the whale. I—I kind of wish you'd be on hand at the back door Sunday mornin' when Simeon comes to take me away. You—you're about the only real friend I've got," she says.

And off she went, for good this time. I pitied her, in spite of her bein' such a dough-head. I knew what sort of a husband that pool-room shark would make. However, there wa'n't nothin' to be done. And next day Cap'n Jonadab was round, madder'n a licked pup. Seems Susannah's lawyer at Orham had sent for her to come right off and see him. Somethin' about the suit, it was. And she was goin' in spite of everything. And with Effie leavin' at the same time, what was we goin' to do over Sunday? and so forth and so on.

Well, we had to do the best we could, that's all. But that Saturday was busy, now I tell you. Sunday mornin' broke fine and clear and, after breakfast was over, I remembered Effie and that 'twas her weddin' day. On the back steps I found her, dressed in all her grandeur, with her packed trunk ready, waitin' for the bridegroom.

"Ain't come yet hey, Effie?" says I.

"No," says she, smilin' and radiant. "It's a little early for him yet, I guess."

I went off to 'tend to the boarders. At half past ten, when I made the back steps again, she was still there. T'other servants was peekin' out of the kitchen windows, grinnin' and passin' remarks.

"Hello!" I calls out. "Not married yet? What's the matter?"

She'd stopped smilin' but she was as chipper as ever, to all appearances.

"I—I guess the horse has gone lame or somethin'," says she. "He'll be here any time now."

There was a cackle from the kitchen windows. I never said nothin'. She'd made her nest; now let her roost on it.

But at twelve Butler hadn't hove in sight. Every hand, male and female, on the place, that wa'n't busy, was hangin' around back of the hotel waitin' and watchin' and ridiculin' and havin' a high time. Them that had errands made it a p'int to cruise past that way.

Lots of the boarders had got wind of the doin's and they was there too.

Effie was settin' on her trunk, tryin' hard to look brave. I went up and spoke to her.

"Come, my girl," says I. "Don't set here no longer. Come into the house and wait. Hadn't you better?"

"No!" says she, loud and defiant like. "No, sir! It's all right. He's a little late, that's all. What do you s'pose I care for a lot of jealous folks like those up there?" wavin' her flipper scornful toward the kitchen.

And then, all to once, she kind of broke down, and says to me, with a pitiful sort of choke in her voice:

"Oh, Mr. Wingate! I can't stand this. Why *don't* he come?"

I tried hard to think of somethin' comfortin' to say, but afore I could h'ist a satisfyin' word out of my hatches I heard the noise of a carriage comin'. Effie heard it too, and so did everybody else. We all looked toward the gate. 'Twas Sim Butler, sure enough, in his buggy and drivin' the same old horse; but settin' alongside of him on the seat was Susannah Debs, the housekeeper. And maybe she didn't look contented with things in gen'ral!

Butler pulled up his horse by the gate. Him and Susannah bowed to all hands. Nobody said anything for a minute. Then Effie bounced off the trunk and down the steps. "Simmie!" she sung out, breathless like, "Simeon Butler, what does this mean?"

The Debs woman straightened up on the seat. "Thank you, marm," says she, chilly as the top section of an ice chest, "I'll request you not to call my husband by his first name."

It was so still you could have heard yourself grow. Effie turned white as a Sunday tablecloth.

"Your—husband?" she gasps. "Your—your *husband?*"

"Yes, marm," purrs the housekeeper. "My husband was what I said. Mr. Butler and me have just been married."

"Sorry, Effie, old girl," puts in Butler, so sassy I'd love to have preached his fun'ral sermon. "Too bad, but fust love's strongest, you know. Susie and me was engaged long afore you come to town."

Then such a hawhaw and whoop bust from the kitchen and fo'castle as you never heard. For a jiffy poor Effie wilted right down. Then she braced up and her black eyes snapped.

"I wish you joy of your bargain, marm," says she to Susannah. "You'd ought to be proud of it. And as for *you,*" she says swingin' round toward the rest of the help, "I—"

"How 'bout that prophet?" hollers somebody.

"Three cheers for the Oriental!" bellers somebody else.

"When you marry the right Butler, fetch him along and let us see him!" whoops another.

She faced 'em all, and I gloried in her spunk.

"When I marry him I *will* come back," says she. "And when I do you'll have to get down on your knees and wait on me. You—and you— Yes, and *you,* too!"

The last two "you's" was hove at Sim and Susannah. Then she turned and marched into the hotel. And the way them hired hands carried on was somethin' scandalous—till I stepped in and took charge of the deck.

That very afternoon I put Effie and her trunk aboard the train. I paid her fare to New York and give her directions how to locate the Van Wedderburns.

"So long, Effie," says I to her. "It's all right. You're enough sight better off. All you want to do now is to work hard and forget all that fortune tellin' foolishness."

She whirled on me like a top.

"Forget it!" she says. "I *guess* I sha'n't forget it! It's comin' true, I tell you—same as all the rest come true. You said yourself there was ten thousand Butlers in the world. Some day the right one—the handsome, high-ranked, distinguished one—will come along, and I'll get him. You wait and see, Mr. Wingate—just you wait and see."

Well, the housekeeper left us that day, of course, and for the rest of that summer the servant question kept me and Jonadab from thinkin' of other things. Course, the reason for the Butler scamp's sudden switch was plain enough. Susannah's lawyer had settled the case with the railroad and, even after his fee was subtracted, there was fifteen hundred left. That was enough sight better'n nine hundred, so Sim figgered when he heard of it; and he hustled to make up with his old girl.

Fifteen hundred dollars doesn't last long with some folks. At the beginnin' of the next spring season both of 'em was round huntin' jobs. Susannah was a fust-rate waitress, so we hired her for that—no more housekeeper for hers, and served her right. As for her husband, we took him on in the stable. He wouldn't have been wuth his salt if it hadn't been for her. She said she'd keep him movin', and she did. She nagged and henpecked him till I'd have been sorry if 'twas anybody else; as 'twas, I got consider'ble satisfaction out of it.

I got one letter from Effie pretty soon after she left, sayin' she liked her new job and that the Van Wedderburns liked her. And that's all I did hear, though Bob himself wrote me in May, sayin' him and Mabel, his wife, had bought a summer cottage in Wapatomac, and me and Jonadab—especially me—must be sure and come to see it and them. He never mentioned his second girl, and I almost forgot her myself.

But one afternoon in early July a big six-cylinder automobile come sailin' down the road and into the Old House yard. A shofer—I b'lieve that's what they call the tribe—was at the helm of it, and on the back seat, lollin' luxurious against the upholstery, was a man and a woman, got up regardless in silk dusters and goggles and veils and prosperity. I never expect to see the Prince of Wales and his wife, but I know how they'd look—after seein' them two.

Jonadab was at the bottom step to welcome 'em, bowin' and scrapin' as if his middle j'int had just been iled. I wa'n't fur astern, and every boarder on deck was all eyes and envy.

The shofer opens the door of the after cock-pit of the machine, and the man gets out fust, treadin' gingerly but grand, as if he was doin' the ground a condescension by steppin' on it. Then he turns to the woman and she slides out, her duds rustlin' like the wind in a scrub oak. The pair sails up the steps, Jonadab and me backin' and fillin' in front of 'em. All the help that could get to a window to peek had knocked off work to do it.

"Ahem!" says the man, pompous as Julius Cæsar—he was big and straight and fine lookin' and had black side whiskers half mast on his cheeks—"Ahem!" says he. "I say, good people, may we have dinner here?"

Well, they tell us time and tide waits for no man, but prob'ly that don't include the nobility. Anyhow, although 'twas long past our reg'lar dinner time, I heard Jonadab tellin' 'em sure and sartin they could. If they wouldn't mind settin' on the piazza or in the front parlor for a spell, he'd have somethin' prepared in a jiffy. So up to the piazza they paraded and come to anchor in a couple of chairs.

"You can have your automobile put right into the barn," I says, "if you want to."

"I don't think it will be necessary—" began the big feller, but the woman interrupted him. She was starin' through her thick veil at the barn door. Sim Butler, in his overalls and ragged shirt-sleeves, was leanin' against that door, interested as the rest of us in what was goin' on.

"I would have it put there, I think," says the woman, lofty and superior. "It is rather dusty, and I think the wheels ought to be washed. Can that man be trusted to wash 'em?" she asks, pointin' kind of scornful at Simeon.

"Yes, marm, I cal'late so," I says. "Here, Sim!" I sung out, callin' Butler over to the steps. "Can you wash the dust off them wheels?"

He said course he could, but he didn't act joyful over the job. The woman seemed some doubtful.

"He looks like a very ignorant, common person," says she, loud and clear, so that everybody, includin' the "ignorant person" himself, could hear her. "However, James'll superintend. James," she orders the shofer, "you see that it is well done, won't you? Make him be very careful."

James looked Butler over from head to foot. "Humph!" he sniffs, contemptuous, with a kind of half grin on his face. "Yes, marm, I'll tend to it."

So he steered the auto into the barn, and Simeon got busy. Judgin' by the sharp language that drifted out through the door 'twas plain that the shofer was superintendin' all right.

Jonadab heaves in sight, bowin', and makes proclamation that dinner is served. The pair riz up majestic and headed for the dinin'-room. The woman was a little astern of her man, and in the hall she turns brisk to me. "Mr. Wingate," she whispers, "Mr. Wingate."

I stared at her. Her voice had sounded sort of familiar ever sence I heard it, but the veil kept a body from seein' what she looked like.

"Hey?" I sings out. "Have I ever—"

"Sh-s-h-h!" she whispers. "Say, Mr. Wingate, that—that Susannah thing is here, ain't she? Have her wait on us, will you, please?"

And she swept the veil off her face. I choked up and staggered bang! against the wall. I swan to man if it wa'n't Effie! *Effie,* in silks and automobiles and gorgeousness!

Afore I could come to myself the two of 'em marched into that dining-room. I heard a grunt and a "Land of love!" from just ahead of me. That was Jonadab. And from all around that dinin'-room come a sort of gasp and then the sound of whisperin'. That was the help.

They took a table by the window, which had been made ready. Down they set, like a king and a queen perchin' on thrones. One of the waiter girls went over to 'em.

But I'd come out of my trance a little mite. The situation was miles ahead of my brain, goodness knows, but the joke of it all was gettin' a grip on me. I remembered what Effie had asked and I spoke up prompt.

"Susannah," says I, "this is a particular job and we're anxious to please. You'd better do the waitin' yourself."

I wish you could have seen the glare that ex-housekeeper give me. For a second I thought we'd have open mutiny. But her place wa'n't any too sartin and she didn't dare risk it. Over she walked to that table, and the fun began.

Jonadab had laid himself out to make that meal a success, but they ate it as if it 'twas pretty poor stuff and not by no means what they fed on every day. They found fault with 'most everything, but most especial with Susannah's waitin'. My! how they did order her around—a mate on a cattle boat wa'n't nothin' to it. And when 'twas all over and they got up to go, Effie says, so's all hands can hear:

"The food here is not so bad, but the service—oh, horrors! However, Albert," says she to the side-whiskered man, "you had better give the girl our usual tip. She looks as if she needed it, poor thing!"

Then they paraded out of the room, and I see Susannah sling the half-dollar the man had left on the table clear to Jericho, it seemed like.

The auto was waitin' by the piazza steps. The shofer and Butler was standin' by it. And when Sim see Effie with her veil throwed back he pretty nigh fell under the wheels he'd been washin' so hard. And he looked as if he wisht they'd run over him.

"Oh, dear!" sighs Effie, lookin' scornful at the wheels. "Not half clean, just as I expected. I knew by the looks of that—that *person* that he wouldn't do it well. Don't give him much, Albert; he ain't earned it."

They climbed into the cockpit, the shofer took the helm, and they was ready to start. But I couldn't let 'em go that way. Out I run.

"Say—say, Effie!" I whispers, eager. "For the goodness' sakes, what's all this mean? Is that your—your—"

"My husband? Yup," she whispers back, her eyes shinin'. "Didn't I tell you to look out for my prophecy? Ain't he handsome and distinguished, just as I said? Good by, Mr. Wingate; maybe I'll see you again some day."

The machinery barked and they got under way. I run along for two steps more.

"But, Effie," says I, "tell me—is his name—?"

She didn't answer. She was watchin' Sim Butler and his wife. Sim had stooped to pick up the quarter the Prince of Wales had hove at him. And that was too much for Susannah, who was watchin' from the window.

"Don't you touch that money!" she screams. "Don't you lay a finger on it! Ain't you got any self-respect at all, yo miser'ble, low-lived—" and so forth and so on. All the way to the front gate I see Effie leanin' out, lookin' and listenin' and smilin'.

Then the machine buzzed off in a typhoon of dust and I went back to Jonadab, who was a livin' catechism of questions which neither one of us could answer.

This yarn ought, I s'pose, to end right here; but it don't. There's a little more of it.

A fortni't later I took a couple of days off and went up to Wapatomac to visit the Van Wedderburns, same as I'd promised. Their "cottage" was pretty nigh big enough for a hotel and was so grand that I, even if I did have on my Sunday frills, was 'most ashamed to ring the doorbell.

But I did ring it, and the feller that opened the door was big and solemn and fine lookin' and had side whiskers. Only this time he wore a tail coat with brass buttons on it.

"How do you do, Mr. Wingate," says he. "Step right in, sir, if you please. Mr. and Mrs. Van Wedderburn are out in the auto, but they'll be back shortly, and very glad to see you, sir, I'm sure. Let me take your grip and hat. Step right into the reception room and wait, if you please, sir. Perhaps," he says, and there was a twinkle in his port eye, though the rest of his face was sober as the front door of a church, "perhaps," says he, "you might wish to speak with my wife a moment. I'll take the liberty of sendin' her to you, sir."

So, as I sat on the gunwale of a blue and gold chair, tryin' to settle whether I was really crazy or only just dreamin', in bounces Effie, rigged up in a servant's cap and apron. She looked polite and demure, but I could see she was just bubblin' with the joy of the whole bus'ness.

"Effie," says I, "Effie, what—what in the world—?"

She giggled. "Yup," she says, "I'm chambermaid here and they treat me fine. Thank you very much for gettin' me the situation."

"But—but them doin's the other day. That automobile—and them silks and satins—and—?"

"Mr. Van Wedderburn lent 'em to me," she said, "him an' his wife. And he lent us the auto and the shofer, too. I'd told him about my troubles at the Old Home House and he thought 'twould be a great joke for me to travel back there like a lady. He's awful fond of a joke—Mr. Van Wedderburn is."

"But that man?" I gasps. "Your husband? That's what you said he was."

"Yes," says she, "he is. We've been married 'most six months now. My prophecy's all come true. And *didn't* I rub it in on that Susannah Debs and her scamp of a Sim? Ho! ho!"

She clasped her hands and pretty nigh danced a jig, she was so tickled.

"But is he a Butler?" I asks.

"Yup," she nods, with another giggle. "He's *a* butler, though his name's Jenkins; and a butler's high rank—higher than chambermaid, anyhow. You see, Mr. Wingate," she adds, "'twas all my fault. When that Oriental Seer man at the show said I was to marry a butler, I forgot to ask him whether you spelt it with a big B or a little one."

MY BROTHER HENRY
AND
GILRAY'S FLOWER-POT

BY J. M. BARRIE

MY BROTHER HENRY

BY J. M. BARRIE

STRICTLY speaking I never had a brother Henry, and yet I can not say that Henry was an impostor. He came into existence in a curious way, and I can think of him now without malice as a child of smoke. The first I heard of Henry was at Pettigrew's house, which is in a London suburb, so conveniently situated that I can go there and back in one day. I was testing some new Cabanas, I remember, when Pettigrew remarked that he had been lunching with a man who knew my brother Henry. Not having any brother but Alexander, I felt that Pettigrew had mistaken the name. "Oh, no," Pettigrew said; "he spoke of Alexander too." Even this did not convince me, and I asked my host for his friend's name. Scudamour was the name of the man, and he had met my brothers Alexander and Henry years before in Paris. Then I remembered Scudamour, and I probably frowned, for I myself was my own brother Henry. I distinctly recalled Scudamour meeting Alexander and me in Paris, and calling me Henry, though my name begins with a J. I explained the mistake to Pettigrew, and here, for the time being, the matter rested. However, I had by no means heard the last of Henry.

Several times afterward I heard from various persons that Scudamour wanted to meet me because he knew my brother Henry. At last we did meet, in Jimmy's chambers; and, almost as soon as he saw me, Scudamour asked where Henry was now. This was precisely what I feared. I am a man who always looks like a boy. There are few persons of my age in London who retain their boyish appearance as long as I have done; indeed, this is the curse of my life. Though I am approaching the age of thirty, I pass for twenty; and I have observed old gentlemen frown at my precocity when I said a good thing or helped myself to a second glass of wine. There was, therefore, nothing surprising in Scudamour's remark, that, when he had the pleasure of meeting Henry, Henry must have been about the age that I had now reached. All would have been well had I explained the real state of affairs to this annoying man; but, unfortunately for myself, I loathe entering upon explanations to anybody about anything. This it is to smoke the Arcadia. When I ring for a time-table and William John brings coals instead, I accept the coals as a substitute. Much, then, did I dread a discussion with Scudamour, his surprise when he heard that I was Henry, and his comments on my youthful appearance. Besides, I was smoking the best of all mixtures. There was no likelihood of my meeting Scudamour again, so the easiest way to get rid of him seemed to be to humor him. I therefore told him that Henry was in India, married, and doing well. "Remember me to Henry when you write to him," was Scudamour's last remark to me that evening.

A few weeks later some one tapped me on the shoulder in Oxford Street. It was Scudamour. "Heard from Henry?" he asked. I said I had heard by the last mail. "Anything particular in the letter?" I felt it would not do to say that there was nothing particular in a letter which had come all the way from India, so I hinted that Henry was having trouble with his wife. By this I meant that her health was bad; but he took it up in another way, and I did not set him right. "Ah, ah!" he said, shaking his head sagaciously; "I'm sorry to hear that. Poor Henry!" "Poor old boy!" was all I could think of replying. "How about the children?" Scudamour asked. "Oh, the children," I said, with what I thought presence of mind, "are coming to England." "To stay with Alexander?" he asked. My answer was that Alexander was expecting them by the middle of next month; and eventually Scudamour went away muttering, "Poor Henry!" In a month or so we met again. "No word of Henry's getting leave of absence?" asked Scudamour. I replied shortly that Henry had gone to live in Bombay, and would not be home for years. He saw that I was brusk, so what does he do but draw me aside for a quiet explanation. "I suppose," he said, "you are annoyed because I told Pettigrew that Henry's wife had run away from him. The fact is, I did it for your good. You see, I happened to make a remark to Pettigrew about your brother Henry, and he said that there was no such person. Of course I laughed at that, and pointed out not only that I had the pleasure of Henry's acquaintance, but that you and I had talked about the old fellow every time we met. 'Well,' Pettigrew said, 'this is a most remarkable thing; for he,' meaning you, 'said to me in this very room, sitting in that very chair, that Alexander was his only brother.' I saw that Pettigrew resented your concealing the existence of your brother Henry from him, so I thought the most friendly thing I could do was to tell him that your reticence was doubtless due to the unhappy state of poor Henry's private affairs. Naturally in the circumstances you did not want to talk about Henry." I shook Scudamour by the hand, telling him that he had acted judiciously; but if I could have stabbed him in the back at that moment I dare say I would have done it.

I did not see Scudamour again for a long time, for I took care to keep out of his way; but I heard first from him and then of him. One day he wrote to me saying that his nephew was going to Bombay, and would I be so good as to give the youth an introduction to my brother Henry? He also asked me to dine with him and his nephew. I declined the dinner, but I sent the nephew the required note of introduction to Henry. The next I heard of Scudamour was from Pettigrew. "By the way," said Pettigrew, "Scudamour is in Edinburgh at present." I trembled, for Edinburgh is where Alexander lives. "What has taken him there?" I asked, with assumed carelessness. Pettigrew believed it was business; "but," he added, "Scudamour asked me to tell you that he meant to call on Alexander, as he was anxious to see Henry's children." A few days afterward I had a telegram from Alexander, who generally uses this means of communication when he corresponds with me.

"Do you know a man, Scudamour? Reply," was what Alexander said. I thought of answering that we had met a man of that name when we were in Paris; but after consideration, I replied boldly: "Know no one of name of Scudamour."

About two months ago I passed Scudamour in Regent Street, and he scowled at me. This I could have borne if there had been no more of Henry; but I knew that Scudamour was now telling everybody about Henry's wife.

By and by I got a letter from an old friend of Alexander's asking me if there was any truth in a report that Alexander was going to Bombay. Soon afterward Alexander wrote to me saying he had been told by several persons that I was going to Bombay. In short, I saw that the time had come for killing Henry. So I told Pettigrew that Henry had died of fever, deeply regretted; and asked him to be sure to tell Scudamour, who had always been interested in the deceased's welfare. Pettigrew afterward told me that he had communicated the sad intelligence to Scudamour. "How did he take it?" I asked. "Well," Pettigrew said, reluctantly, "he told me that when he was up in Edinburgh he did not get on well with Alexander. But he expressed great curiosity as to Henry's children." "Ah," I said, "the children were both drowned in the Forth; a sad affair—we can't bear to talk of it." I am not likely to see much of Scudamour again, nor is Alexander. Scudamour now goes about saying that Henry was the only one of us he really liked.

GILRAY'S FLOWER-POT

BY J. M. BARRIE

I CHARGE Gilray's unreasonableness to his ignoble passion for cigarettes; and the story of his flower-pot has therefore an obvious moral. The want of dignity he displayed about that flower-pot, on his return to London, would have made any one sorry for him. I had my own work to look after, and really could not be tending his chrysanthemum all day. After he came back, however, there was no reasoning with him, and I admit that I never did water his plant, though always intending to do so.

The great mistake was in not leaving the flower-pot in charge of William John. No doubt I readily promised to attend to it, but Gilray deceived me by speaking as if the watering of a plant was the merest pastime. He had to leave London for a short provincial tour, and, as I see now, took advantage of my good nature.

As Gilray had owned his flower-pot for several months, during which time (I take him at his word) he had watered it daily, he must have known he was misleading me. He said that you got into the way of watering a flower-pot regularly just as you wind up your watch. That certainly is not the case. I always wind up my watch, and I never watered the flower-pot. Of course, if I had been living in Gilray's rooms with the thing always before my eyes I might have done so. I proposed to take it into my chambers at the time, but he would not hear of that. Why? How Gilray came by this chrysanthemum I do not inquire, but whether, in the circumstances, he should not have made a clean breast of it to me is another matter. Undoubtedly it was an unusual thing to put a man to the trouble of watering a chrysanthemum daily without giving him its history. My own belief has always been that he got it in exchange for a pair of boots and his old dressing-gown. He hints that it was a present; but, as one who knows him well, I may say that he is the last person a lady would be likely to give a chrysanthemum to. Besides, if he was so proud of the plant he should have stayed at home and watered it himself.

He says that I never meant to water it, which is not only a mistake, but unkind. My plan was to run downstairs immediately after dinner every evening and give it a thorough watering. One thing or another, however, came in the way. I often remembered about the chrysanthemum while I was in the office; but even Gilray could hardly have expected me to ask leave of absence merely to run home and water his plant. You must draw the line somewhere, even in a government office. When I reached home I was tired, inclined to take things easily, and not at all in a proper condition for watering flower-pots. Then Arcadians would drop in. I put it to any sensible man or woman, could I have been expected to give up my friends for the sake of a chrysanthemum? Again, it was my custom of an evening, if not disturbed, to retire with my pipe into my cane chair, and there pass the hours communing with great minds, or, when the mood was on me, trifling with a novel. Often when I was in the middle of a chapter Gilray's flower-pot stood up before my eyes crying for water. He does not believe this, but it is the solemn truth. At those moments it was touch and go, whether I watered his chrysanthemum or not. Where I lost myself was in not hurrying to his rooms at once with a tumbler. I said to myself that I would go when I had finished my pipe, but by that time the flower-pot has escaped my memory. This may have been weakness; all I know is that I should have saved myself much annoyance if I had risen and watered the chrysanthemum there and then. But would it not have been rather hard on me to have had to forsake my books for the sake of Gilray's flowers and flower-pots and plants and things? What right has a man to go and make a garden of his chambers?

All the three weeks he was away, Gilray kept pestering me with letters about his chrysanthemum. He seemed to have no faith in me—a detestable thing in a man who calls himself your friend. I had promised to water his flower-pot; and between friends a promise is surely sufficient. It is not so, however, when Gilray is one of them. I soon hated the sight of my name in his handwriting. It was not as if he said outright that he wrote entirely to know whether I was watering his plant. His references to it were introduced with all the appearance of after-thoughts. Often they took the form of postscripts: "By the way, are you watering my chrysanthemum?" or, "The chrysanthemum ought to be a beauty by this time;" or, "You must be quite an adept now at watering plants." Gilray declares now that, in answer to one of these ingenious epistles, I wrote to him saying that "I had just been watering his chrysanthemum." My belief is that I did no such thing; or, if I did, I meant to water it as soon as I had finished my letter. He has never been able to bring this home to me, he says, because he burned my correspondence. As if a business man would destroy such a letter. It was yet more annoying when Gilray took to post-cards. To hear the postman's knock and then discover, when you are expecting an important communication, that it is only a post-card about a flower-pot—that is really too bad. And then I consider that some of the post-cards bordered upon insult. One of them said, "What about chrysanthemum?—reply at once." This was just like Gilray's overbearing way; but I answered politely, and so far as I knew, truthfully, "Chrysanthemum all right."

Knowing that there was no explaining things to Gilray, I redoubled my exertions to water his flower-pot as the day for his return drew near. Once, indeed, when I rang for water, I could not for the life of me remember what I wanted it for when it was brought. Had I had any forethought I should have left the tumbler stand just as it was to show it to Gilray on his return. But, unfortunately, William John had misunderstood what I wanted the water for, and put a decanter down beside it. Another time I was actually on the stair rushing to Gilray's door, when I met the housekeeper, and, stopping to talk to her, lost my opportunity again. To show how honestly anxious I was to fulfil my promise, I need only add that I was several times awakened in the watches of the night by a haunting consciousness that I had forgotten to water Gilray's flower-pot. On these occasions I spared no trouble to remember again in the morning. I reached out of bed to a chair and turned it upside down, so that the sight of it when I rose might remind me that I had something to do. With the some object I crossed the tongs and poker on the floor. Gilray maintains that instead of playing "fool's tricks" like these ("fool's tricks!") I should have got up and gone at once to his rooms with my water-bottle. What? and disturbed my neighbors? Besides, could I reasonably be expected to risk catching my death of cold for the sake of a wretched chrysanthemum? One reads of men doing such things for young ladies who seek lilies in dangerous ponds or edelweiss on overhanging cliffs. But Gilray was not my sweetheart, nor, I feel certain, any other person's.

I come now to the day prior to Gilray's return. I had just reached the office when I remembered about the chrysanthemum. It was my last chance. If I watered it once I should be in a position to state that, whatever condition it might be in, I had certainly been watering it. I jumped into a hansom, told the cabby to drive to the inn, and twenty minutes afterward had one hand on Gilray's door, while the other held the largest water-can in the house. Opening the door I rushed in. The can nearly fell from my hand. There was no flower-pot! I rang the bell. "Mr. Gilray's chrysanthemum!" I cried. What do you think William John said? He coolly told me that the plant was dead, and had been flung out days ago. I went to the theater that night to keep myself from thinking. All next day I contrived to remain out of Gilray's sight. When we met he was stiff and polite. He did not say a word about the chrysanthemum for a week, and then it all came out with a rush. I let him talk. With the servants flinging out the flower-pots faster than I could water them, what more could I have done? A coolness between us was inevitable. This I regretted, but my mind was made up on one point: I would never do Gilray a favor again.

TEETH

BY MARY HEATON VORSE

TEETH

BY MARY HEATON VORSE

THE incidents of this story occurred during the visit of my sister-in-law and my little niece Agnes. What happened goes to show that, however carefully one may plant a child's mind, the result of the planting, so far as I am able to judge, is uncertain. It is here that figs grow of thistles, and also, alas, thistles of figs.

Estelle, the child's mother, had planted in Agnes all the virtues of childhood and some others, by the means of the newest methods of child culture. In the ground prepared by Estelle, my sister Maria had sown seeds of Christian teaching, reading aloud to Agnes the godly doings of missionaries in the dark places of the earth—a form of reading of which Maria is peculiarly fond, and for which she finds listeners with difficulty. Maria is never tired of expatiating on Agnes' love of good reading, as well as on her other perfections; for Agnes is a very well drilled child. What harvest was reaped from this so carefully planted "garden of a child's mind" (the phrase is Estelle's) I will leave you to judge. It was touching to see that Estelle maintained intact her belief in the efficacy of her training, and saw in what happened only the unfortunate influence of my poor Jimmy. In our house, when anything unchancy occurs, we do not say, "Cherchez la femme," but, "Where is Jimmy?"

The drama began one morning with Maria's arrival at the breakfast-table. She was visibly agitated.

"When I got out of bed this morning," she announced, with a gravity that was portentous, "I started to walk about the floor. I stepped on a small sharp object. It hurt me a great deal—you know, I put my heels down quite hard. I looked to see what hurt me, and here they are!" She displayed two small white objects.

"Why," said Estelle, "those are teeth!"

"Of all things!" said Maria, "teeth! *Small children's teeth!* Will you tell me how children's teeth got in my room?"

"Perhaps Agnes dropped hers there," Osborn suggested.

"No, Osborn, I didn't," said Agnes seriously; and, while she spoke with perfect self-command, a flush spread over her face.

"*Some* one must have dropped them in my room," Maria asserted accusingly. "Why, Edith, it gave me a start when I found a tooth fairly embedded in my heel!"

Maria looked from Jimmy to Agnes, and then back again to Jimmy.

"Do you know anything about these teeth, Jimmy?" she asked.

Here Edith came to the rescue. "It takes away my appetite to talk about such horrid things at the table!" she cried. "Oh, I should think you would have thrown them out of the window, instead of holding an inquest over them at the breakfast-table!"

"That will do, Edith," I said.

Edith is fifteen and is developing a large number of sensibilities. But when Maria has started on a subject, she runs it to earth.

"It must be about time for Agnes to lose hers," she pursued.

"Oh, mama!" cried Agnes, "will I lose a tooth? Will I?" She lifted her upper lip and displayed to view her little white teeth. "I've got one I think is a little eeny teeny weeny bit loose."

"You're interrupting your Aunt Maria," Estelle reminded her daughter.

"How will you pull my tooth out?" asked Agnes, unconcerned. "Will you tie a string around it and to the door, and slam the door?"

"We'll talk about it when the time comes," Estelle replied evenly.

Here Jimmy threw a warning glance at Agnes, but Agnes paid no attention.

"Maud Ellis tied hers to a flat iron and then let it drop," she announced with relish; at which Edith turned up her nose, and Osborn, noticing his sister's disgust, inquired in a pleasant, conversational tone:

"How many teeth has Maud lost?"

"Two," replied Agnes promptly; "and," she continued in a tone of rising exultation, "she's going to lose some more soon."

"It seems to make you pretty happy," said Osborn.

Again Jimmy scowled with meaning, but Agnes looked demurely at her plate.

"Dear me!" Maria mused, "I had forgotten all about children shedding teeth—it's so long since any of our children shed any."

Here Edith ostentatiously left the table.

Jimmy is as transparent as a piece of glass, and I saw easily enough that there was something up between him and Agnes; but I've learned to turn a blind eye to a great many things, so I did not speculate about Jimmy's meaning glances.

Estelle, however, has not been a mother long enough to have learned the valuable lesson of ignoring things.

"What do you suppose Jimmy meant?" she asked me. "I heard him say to Agnes, 'You better cheese it; if they get on to you, they won't let you any more.' 'Why won't they let me?' Agnes asked, and Jimmy said, ' 'Cause grown people won't never let no one do nothing.' 'Anyway,' said Agnes, 'mama's never told me not to!' Now, what do you suppose they were talking about?"

"Why don't you ask Agnes?" I suggested.

I fancied Estelle blushed a little. "I have always told Agnes," she replied, "never to ask questions about things she has overheard, and I must be consistent, Sister Editha."

Estelle and I viewed this incident from opposite sides of the hedge. What surprised me was that Jimmy noticed his cousin at all. Little girls of six and a half do not, as a rule, appeal to twelve-year-old boys of Jimmy's kind, and I saw then and there that there was more to my model niece than appeared on the surface. However, I spent no time over this, for I knew I had yet to have the tooth episode out with Maria. Sure enough, she came to me soon after breakfast, saying:

"Editha, I seldom interfere with your household, and Heaven knows I don't ask my comfort to be considered; but I simply must protest when it comes to having teeth embedded in my bare flesh, *in my own room.*"

Maria spoke as though, had this occurred in any other part of the house, she would not have been surprised enough to protest.

"I don't think you need worry about it, Maria," said I soothingly; "I don't think it will happen again."

"What has happened once," said Maria firmly, "can *always* happen again. I wish to be able to walk across my room in my bare feet without the fear of finding a human tooth in my heel; and I think that you, Editha, owe it to me to make a thorough investigation as to how those teeth got there, with a view to putting a stop to such performances."

"How should you suggest that I go about it, Maria?" I asked, though I knew well enough what Maria wanted. It was to fasten those teeth on Jimmy.

"Put a stop to it; you can do it, if you choose," she said, and walked out of the room with dignity. Hardly had she left, when appeared to me Saraphy, my cook. In her gaunt hand she brandished a feather-duster which had the air of an old hen with ragged tail-feathers, I eyed this object askance.

"Well may ye look!" said my faithful servant. "'Tis the new one ye bought last week! Yes *ma'am,* it is! Miss Maria can talk all she likes about Jimmy, and from now till even about Agnes bein' an angel, but 'tis Agnes is behind doors pickin' feathers out o' new dusters! I don't say nothin' about stealin' pickles with naked hands out o' jars; children is children, and pickles is pickles. If there was a key to the butt'ry, like I've always said there'd oughter be—but there, it ain't about pickles I come to talk, nor about what

Agnes' pockets's full of; for if her ma ain't found out, Lord knows, it ain't no business of mine; all I have to say is that Jimmy's blamed for a lot of things, though 'tis others does 'em! I'm sayin' no names, mind you—but when it comes to sittin' back with my two hands folded, while feathers, bunches and bunches of feathers, ma'am, is picked out o' that duster before my naked eyes, I say Agnes is a sly one, and them feathers is bein' picked out for no good! There's things on foot in this house more than no one knows," Saraphy went on darkly, "but I ain't openin' my mouth, nor will I, not unless it comes to roonin' furniture and pickin' feather-dusters bare. No'm, I ain't openin' *my* mouth, not if all my corks *is* stole."

Having thus unbosomed herself, Saraphy strode from the room, the denuded feather-duster held stiffly in her grim fist.

It was next day that Estelle came to my room, looking very troubled.

"Look," said she, "at these strange lumps I've found stuck all round on the under side of Agnes' little bed!"

Maria took one of the little grayish lumps gingerly in her hand. "That's gum!" she pronounced.

"Gum?" Estelle quavered.

"Gum," Maria asserted firmly; "chewing-gum, Estelle."

They looked at each other a moment; then Estelle said with some dignity, "My child does not chew gum, Sister Maria."

"I don't say she does," said Maria; "I should not have supposed Agnes would. But children are very imitative—look at her now," she added.

Agnes just then came into view, Jimmy with her, although he was apparently unconscious of her presence. Agnes appeared to be munching something. As she came nearer, she stopped.

"My little girl doesn't eat things between meals, does she?" asked Estelle sweetly.

"No, mama," replied Agnes; but Maria stuck to her theory of the inexplicable working of Agnes' jaws.

"Open your mouth, dear," she said, with treacherous sweetness; and, before any one could prevent it, she popped a searching forefinger into her niece's mouth. Unmindful of Agnes' scream, she extracted an able-bodied piece of chewing-gum, which she held aloft between a disgusted thumb and finger.

"Why, Agnes!" cried Estelle. "Why, *Agnes!*"

"You never told me not to, mama; you never told me not to! You never once in your life told me not to chew gum!" cried Agnes, dancing up and down in an agony of self-defense.

"You have been deceiving your mother," said Estelle in grieved tones. She led Agnes out of the room. I have no doubt there was a painful scene. Presently Estelle returned alone.

"I'm afraid, Sister Editha," said she, "it can't go on any longer. I should like to oblige you, and let things work out as you advise; but when it comes to my child deceiving me, chewing *gum* behind my back, then the time has come for me to investigate thoroughly all her actions."

"How on earth, Estelle, did Agnes come to do such a thing?" Maria wished to know.

"She says," Estelle replied, with a sorrowful glance at me, "that Jimmy gave her the gum as a reward for not kissing him; I'm afraid, Sister Editha, that I don't understand Jimmy!"

"I can't imagine, Estelle, how Agnes comes to be so secretive," interrupted Maria.

"It's all new to me," wailed poor Estelle.

You see, I was attacked from all sides—Maria, Saraphy, and Estelle all clamoring to me to find out what it was Jimmy and Agnes were up to; for it was plain as the nose on your face that they were up to something. And here I will say that it was not that innocent angel, Agnes, who gave things away, but my poor, hardened Jimmy. Even at six and a half, Agnes would have known better than to steal furtively from bush to bush if she wanted to hide herself from view. The difference between them was that Agnes was playing a real game of intrigue against the grown-up world, and especially against child culture as embodied in her mother, while Jimmy was hiding principally from imaginary foes, playing over again one of the immortal dramas of childhood.

I tried to hint to Estelle that children, it seemed to me, had some right to privacy in the carrying out of their make-believe games, and that too much prying into their minds begets secrecy; but she only wailed:

"How shall I guide her mind aright if I don't know what's in it? It used to be like a little clear spring of water, but now it's all clouded!"

What was clouding it Estelle was shortly to learn, and from Edith, who had been carrying on investigations of her own. She gave us the benefit of them, with the hostile, chip-on-her-shoulder sort of air which she so affects of late.

"I know," she said, "that Aunt Maria thinks that

Agnes is perfect, and so she probably won't see anything in what I've got to tell. But what I want to know is, does Aunt Estelle know Agnes is making a collection of teeth?"

"What do you mean, Edith?" I asked.

"I mean," replied my daughter, "that she's making a collection of teeth. She's broken her string of coral beads, and she is paying a bead a tooth. Every sort of teeth she buys—dogs' teeth or any kind; but what she likes best is children's teeth. May Ellis' little sister has lost four teeth already, and Agnes has bought 'em all. May says, when she has lost the next two that are loose, her sister is going to have the beads set in a brooch, and I want to know, does Aunt Estelle know about this?"

There was a dramatic pause. Maria said two or three times, "Well, of all things!" and Edith demanded again, "Did you know, Aunt Estelle?"

"No," poor Estelle answered at last, "I didn't!"

"Well," said Edith, with the brutality of her years, "everybody else in town does, then; all the girls are laughing about it. I haven't been able to go anywhere for two days without the girls asking how Agnes' collection of ivories is getting along! Don't frown at me, mother," pursued my unruly child; "I am going to tell Aunt Maria and Aunt Estelle what I think about it. I call it ghastly—that's what I call it!"

"But I never see Agnes playing with any little girls," wailed Estelle.

"She don't play with girls; all she plays with is boys—big boys. She's a very queer child, if she is my cousin. She just sits by the hole in the fence, and swaps beads for teeth through it. And then she goes behind the lilacs, and Jimmy and his gang wait for her there."

"Well," said Maria resignedly, "it only shows how mistaken we can be in people. I should never have dreamed Agnes has tastes like that! She has always seemed like the best, sweetest child, and so interested in things beyond her years! Why, she is always wanting me to read her about the conversion of the heathen. Just this morning I was reading her aloud, for the tenth time, Dr. Leupp's 'A Missionary in the Caribbeans,' and the child is all ears for any good reading of that kind. *Do* you suppose," asked Maria, as a hot, unpleasant thought smote through her consciousness, "do you *suppose* that she is interested only in the savage rites of those cannibals, instead of their conversion?"

I will say, to Estelle's credit, that even at this tragic moment she smiled.

"Well," she announced briskly, "I purpose to find out why my Agnes is making a collection of teeth, and what she does with them after she gets them. Where did you say, Edith, that she and Jimmy play?"

"Behind the lilacs," said Edith. "Saraphy found them out; she says Agnes is sitting on a soap-box, with a croquet-ball in her hand, saying she's going to eat a missionary before the moon is old. All the boys in the neighborhood are there, too—'blacked up like naggurs,' Saraphy says, 'with tails like roosters on 'em.' She says that was a bad day for the feather-dusters of this town when Agnes first clapped her foot in it."

"This is no time for joking, Edith," Maria interposed severely.

"I'm not joking, Aunt Maria. *I* think it's disgusting," replied Edith. "Come and see for yourself."

We bore down on the lilac clump, which leaves a small open space between the hedge and itself. It is the most secluded spot in our grounds. We ducked through the bushes quietly after Edith. As we came near, we heard the cautious, rhythmic beating which I had vaguely noticed of late coming from that part of the garden.

In the light of Maria's pious readings and Saraphy's cryptic utterances, even my dull ears easily recognized this sound as the beating of the tom-tom. Edith lifted a branch of the lilacs, and we peered into the little enclosure beyond. There, sure enough, seated on the soap-box, was Agnes. In one hand she held the croquet-ball; around her throat was a necklace of small white objects. I was near enough to see that the necklace was made of teeth. Beside the soap-box stood a horrid object which I recognized as Jimmy. He was black in the face, and arrayed in savage wise: a billet of wood swung across his shoulder; round his waist was a fringe of feathers. A knot of boys disputed in fierce undertones, while the fat boy whom I knew as Ab solemnly beat the tom-tom with two chicken-bones. They were all blackened and all wore feathers about their waists. Dispute was rife.

"I'm goin' to be et to-day," I heard one say; "Jimmy said I'd be et to-day."

"Aw, go on, you've be'n et already; it's my turn to be et."

"Cheese it, fellers," Jimmy broke in at this point. "Shut up; you make such a row, you c'n be heard a mile." Then, dropping into a tone of lofty grandiloquence, "Only to-day I saw the pale-faced missionary skulking on our trail."

This had a magical effect; the dispute was quelled, and each boy dropped into his part.

"Who brings tribute?" cried Jimmy. "Who has slain an enemy to-day? Who brings pearls for the princess' necklace?"

"I," cried the little boy who had spoken; "I bring tribute." Then, in a casual conversational tone, "I got two teeth offem m' sister; that's why I thought I might be the one to be et."

"Well, you can't, so shut up," said Jimmy tersely. "Bring forward the tribute, Oodoo! Get down and crawl. You better crawl up to the princess, you know."

"Aw, what's the good o' crawlin' up to a girl?" asked the boy.

"See here," said Jimmy, his hand extended in gesture, "that ain't a girl—I don't have girls around. That's the princess o' this tribe. There ain't one o' you kids can sneak feathers like her. She thought o' the human sacrifice, too."

"Aunt Maria read it out of a book to me," Agnes piped up.

"There you are," said Jimmy. "She thought o' the teeth necklace."

"Aw, I don't want ter crawl," said the sulky youth.

"He's gotter crawl, hasn't he, Jimmy?" cried the tribe.

"It's written in the book they crawl," piped Agnes. "If he don't crawl, I won't dance a cannibal dance."

"Well, you dance first, an' I'll crawl after," the boy agreed.

"The princess dances!" cried Jimmy, in the voice of a herald.

Agnes arose from her soap-box. "Here, Jimmy," she said in her distinct way, "you hold my necklace; the teeth keep dropping out of the chewing-gum!" Then she advanced to the middle of the enclosure, lifting her feet high in measure to the tom-tom, rolling her eyes around in savage wildness.

Fascinated, we watched the performance; for Agnes, the decorous, the well-behaved, the model child, was changed before our eyes into a wild, primitive aborigine, while, with savage gestures, she danced what seemed a cross between some mad, primeval cake-walk and the Indian war-dance seen in the shows of Buffalo Bill. In its way, it was quite a triumphant performance, but it did not so appear to Estelle. For a time she watched her daughter in a frozen fascination, then she cried out:

"Agnes!" And at her word the heart of Africa died. It was like the things one reads in fairy stories —the enchantment was over. What had been brave cannibal warriors turned into shamefaced little boys blackened up with burnt cork, who crawled into bushes. Everywhere one saw the hinder parts of breeches in full retreat. The tom-tom was deserted, the soap-box tipped over, the croquet-ball rolled lazily across the enclosure, while tufts of feathers, pulled off in the scramble, festooned the lilac-bushes. Jimmy and Agnes alone remained face to face with the avenging Estelle.

It is in crises like these, I think, that the child-culturist falls down. I shall always feel that Estelle's "What was my little girl doing?" was a highly inadequate remark under the circumstances, and opened the gate to Agnes' indignant roar, starting with the long-drawn, ascendant "O-o-o!" of childhood, and ending with "I can't ever have any fun!"

"This is not a suitable sort of fun," Estelle told her daughter sternly, as she led away the screaming child; and as she walked off, Maria thought it an appropriate time to say to me:

"I am disappointed in the results of Estelle's training. In a crisis she lacks firmness as much as you do, Editha."

Later in the afternoon Estelle came to me. "I am sure you'll understand, Sister Editha, why I feel I must cut my visit short. Agnes' nerves are quite unstrung, and, while I think Jimmy is a dear little boy, he is too old to be a companion for Agnes." Which, of course, was just another way of saying that everything that had happened was, somehow or other, all Jimmy's fault again.

After Agnes had gone, Jimmy followed me to my room. He walked about, pulling a leaf from my plant and fingering things upon my dressing-table. I saw that he was getting ready to say something. At last he jerked it out:

"Have you gotter little box?"

"How big a box, Jimmy?" I asked. "What for?"

He hesitated, with momentary distrust; then he decided to risk it.

"Big enough to hold this," he answered, defiance lurking in his tone. He carefully took out of his pocket a piece of string. Along its length were lumps of chewing-gum, and in each lump of gum was set a tooth. It was the princess' necklace.

"Sealing-wax would er held 'em better," Jimmy mused, as he looked at the treasure. Then he burst out:

"Aunt Estelle makes me sick! She wouldn't let her have it; so I'm going to save it for next year."

Then, as he put the necklace into the box, there sounded the first note of sentiment that I had ever heard from Jimmy; for it was with something like tenderness that he said:

"She worked hard to collect those teeth!"

THE KING OF BOYVILLE

BY WILLIAM ALLEN WHITE

THE KING OF BOYVILLE

BY WILLIAM ALLEN WHITE

BOYS who are born in a small town are born free and equal. In the big city it may be different; there are doubtless good little boys who disdain bad little boys, and poor little boys who are never to be noticed under any circumstances. But in a small town every boy, good or bad, rich or poor, stands among boys of his own merits. The son of the banker who owns the turning-pole in the back yard does homage to the baker's boy who can sit on the bar and drop down and catch by his legs; while the good little boy who is kept in wide collars and cuffs by a mistaken mother gazes through the white paling of his father's fence at the troop headed for the swimming-hole, and pays all the reverence which his dwarfed nature can muster to the sign of two fingers.

In the social order of boys who live in country towns a boy is measured by what he can do, and not by what his father is. And so Winfield Hancock Pennington, whose boy name was Piggy Pennington, was the King of Boyville. For Piggy could walk on his hands, curling one foot gracefully over his back, and pointing the other one straight in the air; he could hang by his heels on a flying trapeze; he could chin a pole so many times that no one could count the number; he could turn a somersault in the air from the level ground, both backward and forward; he could "tread" water, and "lay" his hair; he could hit any marble in any ring from "taws" and "knucks" down; and, better than all, he could cut his initials in the ice on skates, and whirl round and round so many times that he looked like an animated shadow, when he would dart away up the stream, his red "comfort" flapping behind him like a laugh of defiance. In the story-books such a boy would be the son of a widowed mother, and turn out very good or very bad; but Piggy was not a story-book boy, and his father kept a grocery store, from which Piggy used to steal so many dates that the boys said his father must have cut up the almanac to supply him. As he never gave the goodies to the other boys, but kept them for his own use, his name of "Piggy" was his by all the rights of Boyville.

There was one thing Piggy Pennington could not do, and it was the one of all things that he most wished he could do; he could not, under any circumstances, say three consecutive and coherent words to any girl under fifteen and over nine. He was invited, with nearly all the boys of his age in town, to children's parties. And while any other boy, whose only accomplishment was turning a cart-wheel, or skinning the cat backward, or, at most, hanging by one leg and turning a handspring, could boldly ask a girl if he could see her home, Piggy had to get his hat and sneak out of the house when the company broke up. He would comfort himself by walking along the opposite side of the street from some couple, while he talked in monosyllables about a joke which he and the boy knew, but which was always a secret to the girl. Even after school Piggy could not join the select coterie of boys who followed the girls down through town to the post-office. He could not tease the girls about absent boys at such times, and made up rhymes like

> "First the cat and then her tail;
> Jimmie Sears and Maggie Hale,"

and shout them out for the crowd to hear. Instead of joining the courtly troupe, Piggy Pennington went off with the boys who really didn't care for such things, and fought, or played "tracks up," or wrestled his way leisurely home in time to get in his "night wood." But his heart was not in these pastimes. It was with a red shawl of peculiar shade, that was wending its way to the post-office and back, to a home in one of the few two-story houses in the little town. Time and again had Piggy tried to make some sign to let his feelings be known, but every time he had failed. Lying in wait for her at corners and suddenly breaking upon her with a glory of backward and forward somersaults did not convey the state of his heart. Hanging by his heels from an apple-tree limb over the sidewalk in front of her, unexpectedly, did not tell the tender tale for which his lips could find no words. And the nearest he could come to an expression of the longing in his breast was to cut her initials in the ice beside his own when she came wobbling past on some other boy's arm. But she would not look at the initials, and the chirography of his skates was so indistinct that it required a key; and, everything put together, poor Piggy was no nearer a declaration at the end of the winter than he had been at the beginning of autumn. So only one heart beat with but a single thought, and the other took motto candy and valentines and red apples and picture-cards and other tokens of esteem from other boys, and beat on with any number of thoughts, entirely immaterial to the uses of this narrative. But Piggy Pennington did not take to the enchantment of corn-silk cigarettes, and rattan and grapevine cigars. He tried to sing, and wailed dismal ballads about "The Gipsy's Warning," and "The child in the grave with its mother," and "She's a daisy, she's a darling, she's a dumpling, she's a lamb," whenever he was in hearing distance of his Heart's Desire, in the hope of conveying to her some hint of the state of his affections; but it was useless. Even when, as he passed her house in the gloaming, he tried to whistle plaintively, his notes brought forth no responsive echo.

One morning in the late spring he spent half an hour before breakfast among his mother's roses, which were just in first bloom. He had taken out there all the wire from an old broom and all his kite-string. His mother had to call him three times before he would leave his work. The youngster was the first to leave the table, and by eight o'clock he was at his task again. Before the first school-bell had rung, Piggy Pennington was bound for the schoolhouse with a strange-looking parcel under his arm. He tried to put his coat over it, but it stuck out, and the newspaper that was wrapped around it bulged into so many corners that it looked like a home-tied bundle of laundry.

"What you got?" asked the freckle-faced boy who was learning at Piggy's feet how to do the "muscle-grind" on the turning-pole.

But Piggy Pennington was the King of Boyville, and he had a right to look straight ahead of him as if he did not hear the question, and say, "Lookie here, Mealy, I wish you would go and tell Abe I want him to hurry up, for I want to see him."

"Abe" was Piggy's nearest friend. His other name was Carpenter. Piggy only wished to be rid of the freckle-faced boy. But the freckle-faced boy was not used to royalty and its ways, so he pushed his inquiry.

"Say, Piggy, have you got your red ball-pants in that bundle?"

There was no reply. The freckle-faced boy grew tired of tattooing with a stick as they walked beside a paling fence, so he began touching every tree on the other side of the path with his fingers. They had gone a block when the freckle-faced boy could stand it no longer, and said:

"Say, Piggy, you needn't be so smart about your old bundle; now, honest, Piggy, what have you got in that bundle?"

"Aw—soft soap; take a bite—good fer your appetite," said the King, as he faced about and drew up his left cheek and lower eyelid pugnaciously. The freckle-faced boy saw he would have to fight if he stayed, so he turned to go, and said, as though nothing had happened, "Where do you suppose old Abe is anyhow?"

Just before school was called, Piggy Pennington was playing "scrub" with all his might, and a little girl—his Heart's Desire—was taking out of her desk a wreath of roses tied to a shaky wire frame. There was a crowd of girls round her admiring it, and speculating about the probable author of the gift; but to these she did not show the patent-medicine card on which was scrawled over the druggist's advertisement, "Yours truly, W. H. P."

When the last bell rang, Piggy Pennington was the last boy in, and he did not look toward the desk where he had put the flowers until after the singing. Then he stole a sidewise glance that way, and his Heart's Desire was deep in her geography. It was an age before she filed past him with the "B" class in geography, and took a seat directly in front of him, where he could look at her all the time, unobserved by her. Once she squirmed in her place and looked toward him, but Piggy Pennington was head over heels in the "Iser rolling rapidly." When their eyes did meet at last, just as Piggy, leading the marching around the room, was at the door to go out for recess, the thrill amounted to a shock that sent him whirling in a pinwheel of handsprings toward the ballground, shouting "scrub—first bat, first bat, first bat," from sheer bubbling joy. Piggy made four tallies that recess, and the other boys couldn't have put him out if they had used a hand-grenade or a Babcock fire-extinguisher.

He received four distinct shots that day from the eyes of his Heart's Desire, and the last one sent him home on the run, tripping up every primary urchin whom he found tagging along by the way, and whooping at the top of his voice. When his friends met in his barn, some fifteen minutes later, Piggy tried to turn a double somersault from his spring-board, to the admiration of the crowd, and was only calmed by falling with his full weight on his head and shoulders at the edge of the hay, with the life nearly jolted out of his little body.

The next morning Piggy Pennington astonished his friends by bringing a big armful of red and yellow and pink and white roses to school. He had never done this before; and when he had run the gantlet of the big boys, who were not afraid to steal them from him, he made straight for his schoolroom, and stood holding them in his hands while the girls gathered about him, teasing for the beauties. It was nearly time for the last bell to ring, and Piggy knew that his Heart's Desire would be in the room by the time he got there. He was not mistaken. But Heart's Desire did not clamor with the other girls for one of the roses. Piggy stood off their pleadings as long as he could with "Naw"; "Why, naw, of course I won't"; "Naw; what I want to give you one for?" and "Go away from here, I tell you." Still Heart's Desire did not ask for her flowers. There were but a few moments left before school would be called to order, and in desperation Piggy gave one rose away. It was not a very pretty rose, but he hoped she would see that the others were to be given away, and ask for one. But she, his Heart's Desire, stood near a window talking to the freckle-faced boy. Then Piggy gave away one rose after another. As the last bell began to ring he gave them to the boys, as the girls were all supplied. And still she came not. There was one rose left, the most beautiful of all. She went to her desk, and as the teacher came in, bell in hand, Piggy surprised himself, the teacher, and the school by laying the beautiful flower, without a word, on the teacher's desk. That day was a dark day. When a new boy, who didn't belong to the school, came up at recess to play, Piggy shuffled over to him and asked gruffly:

"What's your name?"

"Puddin' 'n' tame, ast me ag'n an' I'll tell you the same," said the new boy, and then there was a fight. It didn't soothe Piggy's feelings one bit that he whipped the new boy, for the new boy was smaller than Piggy. And he dared not turn his flushed face toward his Heart's Desire. It was almost four o'clock when Piggy Pennington walked to the master's desk to get him to work out a problem, and as he passed the desk of Heart's Desire he dropped a note in her lap. It read:

"Are you mad?"

But he dared not look for an answer as they marched out that night, so he contented himself with punching the boy ahead of him with a pin, and stepping on his heels when they were in the back part of the room, where the teacher would not see him. The King of Boyville walked home alone that evening. The courtiers saw plainly that his Majesty was troubled.

So his lonely way was strewn with broken stick-horses which he took from the little boys, and was marked with trees adorned with the string which he took from other youngsters who ran across his pathway playing horse. In his barn he sat listlessly on a nail-keg, while Abe and the freckle-faced boy did their deeds of daring on the rings and the trapeze. Only when the new boy came in did Piggy arouse himself to mount the flying bar, and, swinging in it to the very rafters, drop and hang by his knees, and again drop from his knees, catching his ankle in the angle of the rope where it meets the swinging bar. That was to awe the new boy.

After this feat the King was quiet.

At dusk, when the evening chores were done, Piggy Pennington walked past the home of his Heart's Desire, and howled out a doleful ballad which began:

> "You ask what makes this darky wee-eep,
> Why he like others am not gay."

But a man on the sidewalk, passing, said: "Well, son, that's pretty good; but wouldn't you just as lief sing as to make that noise?" So the King went to bed with a heavy heart.

He took that heart to school with him the next morning, and dragged it over the school-ground, playing crack-the-whip and "stinkbase." But when he saw Heart's Desire wearing in her hair one of the white roses from his mother's garden—the Penningtons had the only white roses in the little town—he knew it was from the wreath he had given her, and so light was his boyish heart that it was with an effort that he kept it out of his throat. There were smiles and smiles that day. During the singing they began, and every time she came past him from a class, and every time he could pry his eyes behind her geography or her grammar, a flood of gladness swept over his soul.

That night Piggy Pennington followed the girls from the schoolhouse to the post-office, and in a burst of enthusiasm walked on his hands in front of the crowd for nearly half a block.

When his Heart's Desire said, "Oh! ain't you afraid you'll hurt yourself doing that?" Piggy pretended not to hear her, and said to the boys:

"Aw, that ain't nuthin'; come down to my barn and I'll do somepin' that'll make your head swim."

He was too exuberant to contain himself, and when he left the girls he started to run after a stray chicken that happened along, and ran till he was out of breath. He did not mean to run in the direction his Heart's Desire had taken, but he turned a corner and came up with her suddenly.

Her eyes beamed upon him, and he could not run away as he wished. She made room for him on the sidewalk, and he could do nothing but walk beside her. For a block they were so embarrassed that neither spoke.

It was Piggy who broke the silence. His words came from his heart. He had not yet learned to speak otherwise.

"Where's your rose?" he asked, not seeing it.

"What rose?" said the girl, as though she had never in her short life heard of such an absurd thing as a rose.

"Oh, you know," returned the boy, stepping irregularly to make the tips of his toes come on the cracks in the sidewalk. There was another pause, during which Piggy picked up a pebble and threw it at a bird in a tree.

His heart was sinking rapidly.

"Oh, that rose?" said his Heart's Desire, turning full upon him with the enchantment of her childish eyes. "Why, here it is in my grammar. I'm taking it to keep with the others. Why?"

"Oh, nuthin' much," replied the boy. "I bet you can't do this," he added, as he glowed up into her eyes from an impulsive handspring.

And thus the King of Boyville first set his light little foot upon the soil of an unknown country.

THE WIDOW'S CRUISE

BY F. R. STOCKTON

THE WIDOW'S CRUISE

BY F. R. STOCKTON

THE Widow Ducket lived in a small village about ten miles from the New Jersey seacoast. In this village she was born, here she had married and buried her husband, and here she expected somebody to bury her; but she was in no hurry for this, for she had scarcely reached middle age. She was a tall woman with no apparent fat in her composition, and full of activity, both muscular and mental.

She rose at six o'clock in the morning, cooked breakfast, set the table, washed the dishes when the meal was over, milked, churned, swept, washed, ironed, worked in her little garden, attended to the flowers in the front yard and in the afternoon knitted and quilted and sewed, and after tea she either went to see her neighbors or had them come to see her. When it was really dark she lighted the lamp in her parlor and read for an hour, and if it happened to be one of Miss Mary Wilkins's books that she read she expressed doubts as to the realism of the characters therein described.

These doubts she expressed to Dorcas Networthy, who was a small, plump woman, with a solemn face, who had lived with the widow for many years and who had become her devoted disciple. Whatever the widow did, that also did Dorcas—not so well, for her heart told her she could never expect to do that, but with a yearning anxiety to do everything as well as she could.

She rose at five minutes past six, and in a subsidiary way she helped to get the breakfast, to eat it, to wash up the dishes, to work in the garden, to quilt, to sew, to visit and receive, and no one could have tried harder than she did to keep awake when the widow read aloud in the evening.

All these things happened every day in the summer-time, but in the winter the widow and Dorcas cleared the snow from their little front path instead of attending to the flowers, and in the evening they lighted a fire as well as a lamp in the parlor.

Sometimes, however, something different happened, but this was not often, only a few times in the year. One of the different things occurred when Mrs. Ducket and Dorcas were sitting on their little front porch one summer afternoon, one on the little bench on one side of the door, and the other on the little bench on the other side of the door, each waiting until she should hear the clock strike five, to prepare tea. But it was not yet a quarter to five when a one-horse wagon containing four men came slowly down the street. Dorcas first saw the wagon, and she instantly stopped knitting.

"Mercy on me!" she exclaimed. "Whoever those people are, they are strangers here, and they don't know where to stop, for they first go to one side of the street and then to the other."

The widow looked around sharply. "Humph!" said she. "Those men are sailormen. You might see that in a twinklin' of an eye. Sailormen always drive that way, because that is the way they sail ships. They first tack in one direction and then in another."

"Mr. Ducket didn't like the sea?" remarked Dorcas, for about the three hundredth time.

"No, he didn't," answered the widow, for about the two hundred and fiftieth time, for there had been occasions when she thought Dorcas put this question inopportunely. "He hated it, and he was drowned in it through trustin' a sailorman, which I never did nor shall. Do you really believe those men are comin' here?"

"Upon my word I do!" said Dorcas, and her opinion was correct.

The wagon drew up in front of Mrs. Ducket's little white house, and the two women sat rigidly, their hands in their laps, staring at the man who drove.

This was an elderly personage with whitish hair, and under his chin a thin whitish beard, which waved in the gentle breeze and gave Dorcas the idea that his head was filled with hair which was leaking out from below.

"Is this the Widow Ducket's?" inquired this elderly man, in a strong, penetrating voice.

"That's my name," said the widow, and laying her knitting on the bench beside her, she went to the gate. Dorcas also laid her knitting on the bench beside her and went to the gate.

"I was told," said the elderly man, "at a house we touched at about a quarter of a mile back, that the Widow Ducket's was the only house in this village where there was any chance of me and my mates getting a meal. We are four sailors, and we are making from the bay over to Cuppertown, and that's eight miles ahead yet, and we are all pretty sharp set for something to eat."

"This is the place," said the widow, "and I do give meals if there is enough in the house and everything comes handy,"

"Does everything come handy to-day?" said he.

"It does," said she, "and you can hitch your horse and come in; but I haven't got anything for him."

"Oh, that's all right," said the man, "we brought along stores for him, so we'll just make fast and then come in."

The two women hurried into the house in a state of bustling preparation, for the furnishing of this meal meant one dollar in cash.

The four mariners, all elderly men, descended from the wagon, each one scrambling with alacrity over a different wheel.

A box of broken ship-biscuit was brought out and put on the ground in front of the horse, who immediately set himself to eating with great satisfaction.

Tea was a little late that day, because there were six persons to provide for instead of two, but it was a good meal, and after the four seamen had washed their hands and faces at the pump in the back yard and had wiped them on two towels furnished by Dorcas, they all came in and sat down. Mrs. Ducket seated herself at the head of the table with the dignity proper to the mistress of the house, and Dorcas seated herself at the other end with the dignity proper to the disciple of the mistress. No service was necessary, for everything that was to be eaten or drunk was on the table.

When each of the elderly mariners had had as much

bread and butter, quickly baked soda-biscuit, dried beef, cold ham, cold tongue, and preserved fruit of every variety known, as his storage capacity would permit, the mariner in command, Captain Bird, pushed back his chair, whereupon the other mariners pushed back their chairs.

"Madam," said Captain Bird, "we have all made a good meal, which didn't need to be no better nor more of it, and we're satisfied; but that horse out there has not had time to rest himself enough to go the eight miles that lies ahead of us, so, if it's all the same to you and this good lady, we'd like to sit on that front porch awhile and smoke our pipes. I was a-looking at that porch when I came in, and I bethought to myself what a rare good place it was to smoke a pipe in."

"There's pipes been smoked there," said the widow, rising, "and it can be done again. Inside the house I don't allow tobacco, but on the porch neither of us minds."

So the four captains betook themselves to the porch, two of them seating themselves on the little bench on one side of the door, and two of them on the little bench on the other side of the door, and lighted their pipes.

"Shall we clear off the table and wash up the dishes," said Dorcas, "or wait until they are gone?"

"We will wait until they are gone," said the widow, "for now that they are here we might as well have a bit of a chat with them. When a sailorman lights his pipe he is generally willin' to talk, but when he is eatin' you can't get a word out of him."

Without thinking it necessary to ask permission, for the house belonged to her, the Widow Ducket brought a chair and put it in the hall close to the open front door, and Dorcas brought another chair and seated herself by the side of the widow.

"Do all you sailormen belong down there at the bay?" asked Mrs. Ducket; thus the conversation began, and in a few minutes it had reached a point at which Captain Bird thought it proper to say that a great many strange things happen to seamen sailing on the sea which lands-people never dream of.

"Such as anything in particular?" asked the widow, at which remark Dorcas clasped her hands in expectancy.

At this question each of the mariners took his pipe from his mouth and gazed upon the floor in thought.

"There's a good many strange things happened to me and my mates at sea. Would you and that other lady like to hear any of them?" asked Captain Bird.

"We would like to hear them if they are true," said the widow.

"There's nothing happened to me and my mates that isn't true," said Captain Bird, "and here is something that once happened to me: I was on a whaling v'yage when a big sperm-whale, just as mad as a fiery bull, came at us, head on, and struck the ship at the stern with such tremendous force that his head crashed right through her timbers and he went nearly half his length into her hull. The hold was mostly filled with empty barrels, for we was just beginning our v'yage, and when he had made kindling-wood of these there was room enough for him. We all expected that it wouldn't take five minutes for the vessel to fill and go to the bottom, and we made ready to take to the boats; but it turned out we didn't need to take to no boats, for as fast as the water rushed into the hold of the ship, that whale drank it and squirted it up through the two blow-holes in the top of his head, and as there was an open hatchway just over his head, the water all went into the sea again, and that whale kept working day and night pumping the water out until we beached the vessel on the island of Trinidad—the whale helping us wonderful on our way over by the powerful working of his tail, which, being outside in the water, acted like a propeller. I don't believe anything stranger than that ever happened to a whaling-ship."

"No," said the widow, "I don't believe anything ever did."

Captain Bird now looked at Captain Sanderson, and the latter took his pipe out of his mouth and said that in all his sailing around the world he had never known anything queerer than what happened to a big steamship he chanced to be on, which ran into an island in a fog. Everybody on board thought the ship was wrecked, but it had twin screws, and was going at such a tremendous speed that it turned the island entirely upside down and sailed over it, and he had heard tell that even now people sailing over the spot could look down into the water and see the roots of the trees and the cellars of the houses.

Captain Sanderson now put his pipe back into his mouth, and Captain Burress took out his pipe.

"I was once in an obelisk-ship," said he, "that used to trade regular between Egypt and New York, carrying obelisks. We had a big obelisk on board. The way they ship obelisks is to make a hole in the stern of the ship, and run the obelisk in, p'inted end foremost; and this obelisk filled up nearly the whole of that ship from stern to bow. We was about ten days out, and sailing afore a northeast gale with the engines at full speed, when suddenly we spied breakers ahead, and our captain saw we was about to run on a bank. Now if we hadn't had an obelisk on board we might have sailed over that bank, but the captain knew that with an obelisk on board we drew too much water for this, and that we'd be wrecked in about fifty-five seconds if something wasn't done quick. So he had to do something quick, and this is what he did: He ordered all steam on, and drove slam-bang on that bank. Just as he expected, we stopped so suddint that that big obelisk bounced for'ard, its p'inted end foremost, and went clean through the bow and shot out into the sea. The minute it did that the vessel was so lightened that it rose in the water and we then steamed over the bank. There was one man knocked overboard by the shock when we struck, but as soon as we missed him we went back after him and we got him all right. You see, when that obelisk went overboard, its butt-end, which was heaviest, went down first, and when it touched the bottom it just stood there, and as it was such a big obelisk there was about five and a half feet of it stuck out of the water. The man who was knocked overboard he just swum for that obelisk and he climbed up the hiryglyphics. It was a mighty fine obelisk, and the Egyptians had cut their hiryglyphics good and deep, so that the man could get hand and foot hold; and when we got to him and took him off, he was sitting high and dry on the p'inted end of that obelisk. It was a great pity about the obelisk, for it was a good obelisk, but as I never heard the company tried to raise it, I expect it is standing there yet."

Captain Burress now put his pipe back into his mouth and looked at Captain Jenkinson, who removed his pipe and said:

"The queerest thing that ever happened to me was about a shark. We was off the Banks, and the time of year was July, and the ice was coming down, and we got in among a lot of it. Not far away, off our weather bow, there was a little iceberg which had such a queerness about it that the captain and three men went in a boat to look at it. The ice was mighty clear ice, and you could see almost through it, and right inside of it, not more than three feet above the water-line, and about two feet, or maybe twenty inches, inside the ice, was a whopping big shark, about fourteen feet long,—a regular man-eater,—frozen in there hard and fast. 'Bless my soul,' said the captain, 'this is a wonderful curiosity, and I'm going to git him out.' Just then one of the men said he saw that shark wink, but the captain wouldn't believe him, for he said that shark was frozen stiff and hard and couldn't wink. You see, the captain had his own idees about things, and he knew that whales was warm-blooded and would freeze if they was shut up in ice, but he forgot that sharks was not whales and that they're cold-blooded just like toads. And there is toads that has been shut up in rocks for thousands of years, and they stayed alive, no matter how cold the place was, because they was cold-blooded, and when the rocks was split, out hopped the frog. But, as I said before, the captain forgot sharks was cold-blooded, and he determined to git that one out.

"Now you both know, being housekeepers, that if you take a needle and drive it into a hunk of ice you can split it. The captain had a sail-needle with him, and so he drove it into the iceberg right alongside of the shark and split it. Now the minute he did it he knew that the man was right when he said he saw the shark wink, for it flopped out of that iceberg quicker nor a flash of lightning."

"What a happy fish he must have been!" ejaculated Dorcas, forgetful of precedent, so great was her emotion.

"Yes," said Captain Jenkinson, "it was a happy fish enough, but it wasn't a happy captain. You see, that shark hadn't had anything to eat, perhaps for a thousand years, until the captain came along with his sail-needle."

"Surely you sailormen do see strange things," now said the widow, "and the strangest thing about them is that they are true."

"Yes, indeed," said Dorcas, "that is the most wonderful thing."

"You wouldn't suppose," said the Widow Ducket, glancing from one bench of mariners to the other, "that I have a sea-story to tell, but I have, and if you like I will tell it to you."

Captain Bird looked up a little surprised.

"We would like to hear it—indeed, we would, madam," said he.

"Ay, ay!" said Captain Burress, and the two other mariners nodded.

"It was a good while ago," she said, "when I was living on the shore near the head of the bay, that my husband was away and I was left alone in the house.

One mornin' my sister-in-law, who lived on the other side of the bay, sent me word by a boy on a horse that she hadn't any oil in the house to fill the lamp that she always put in the window to light her husband home, who was a fisherman, and if I would send her some by the boy she would pay me back as soon as they bought oil. The boy said he would stop on his way home and take the oil to her, but he never did stop, or perhaps he never went back, and about five o'clock I began to get dreadfully worried, for I knew if that lamp wasn't in my sister-in-law's window by dark she might be a widow before midnight. So I said to myself, 'I've got to get that oil to her, no matter what happens or how it's done.' Of course I couldn't tell what might happen, but there was only one way it could be done, and that was for me to get into the boat that was tied to the post down by the water, and take it to her, for it was too far for me to walk around by the head of the bay. Now, the trouble was, I didn't know no more about a boat and the managin' of it than any one of you sailormen knows about clear-starchin'. But there wasn't no use of thinkin' what I knew and what I didn't know, for I had to take it to her, and there was no way of doin' it except in that boat. So I filled a gallon can, for I thought I might as well take enough while I was about it, and I went down to the water and I unhitched that boat and I put the oil-can into her, and then I got in, and off I started, and when I was about a quarter of a mile from the shore—"

"Madam," interrupted Captain Bird, "did you row or—or was there a sail to the boat?"

The widow looked at the questioner for a moment.

"No," said she, "I didn't row. I forgot to bring the oars from the house; but it didn't matter, for I didn't know how to use them, and if there had been a sail I couldn't have put it up, for I didn't know how to use it, either. I used the rudder to make the boat go. The rudder was the only thing I knew anything about. I'd held a rudder when I was a little girl, and I knew how to work it. So I just took hold of the handle of the rudder and turned it round and round, and that made the boat go ahead, you know, and—"

"Madam!" exclaimed Captain Bird, and the other elderly mariners took their pipes from their mouths.

"Yes, that is the way I did it," continued the widow, briskly. "Big steamships are made to go by a propeller turning round and round at their back ends, and I made the rudder work in the same way, and I got along very well, too, until suddenly, when I was about a quarter of a mile from the shore, a most terrible and awful storm arose. There must have been a typhoon or a cyclone out at sea, for the waves came up the bay bigger than houses, and when they got to the head of the bay they turned around and tried to get out to sea again. So in this way they continually met, and made the most awful and roarin' pilin' up of waves that ever was known.

"My little boat was pitched about as if it had been a feather in a breeze, and when the front part of it was cleavin' itself down into the water the hind part was stickin' up until the rudder whizzed around like a patent churn with no milk in it. The thunder began to roar and the lightnin' flashed, and three sea-gulls, so nearly frightened to death that they began to turn up the whites of their eyes, flew down and sat on one of the seats of the boat, forgettin' in that awful moment that man was their nat'ral enemy. I had a couple of biscuits in my pocket, because I had thought I might want a bite in crossing, and I crumpled up one of these and fed the poor creatures. Then I began to wonder what I was goin' to do, for things were gettin' awfuller and awfuller every instant, and the little boat was a-heavin' and a-pitchin' and a-rollin' and h'istin' itself up, first on one end and then on the other, to such an extent that if I hadn't kept tight hold of the rudder-handle I'd slipped off the seat I was sittin' on.

"All of a sudden I remembered that oil in the can; but just as I was puttin' my fingers on the cork my conscience smote me. 'Am I goin' to use this oil,' I said to myself, 'and let my sister-in-law's husband be wrecked for want of it?' And then I thought that he wouldn't want it all that night, and perhaps they would buy oil the next day, and so I poured out about a tumblerful of it on the water, and I can just tell you sailormen that you never saw anything act as prompt as that did. In three seconds, or perhaps five, the water all around me, for the distance of a small front yard, was just as flat as a table and as smooth as glass, and so invitin' in appearance that the three gulls jumped out of the boat and began to swim about on it, primin' their feathers and lookin' at themselves in the transparent depths, though I must say that one of them made an awful face as he dipped his bill into the water and tasted kerosene.

"Now I had time to sit quiet in the midst of the placid space I had made for myself, and rest from workin' of the rudder. Truly it was a wonderful and marvelous thing to look at. The waves was roarin' and leapin' up all around me higher than the roof of this house, and sometimes their tops would reach over so that they nearly met and shut out all view of the stormy sky, which seemed as if it was bein' torn to pieces by blazin' lightnin', while the thunder pealed so tremendous that it almost drowned the roar of the waves. Not only above and all around me was everything terrific and fearful, but even under me it was the same, for there was a big crack in the bottom of the boat as wide as my hand, and through this I could see down into the water beneath, and there was—"

"Madam!" ejaculated Captain Bird, the hand which had been holding his pipe a few inches from his mouth now dropping to his knee; and at this motion the hands which held the pipes of the three other mariners dropped to their knees.

"Of course it sounds strange," continued the widow, "but I know that people can see down into clear water, and the water under me was clear, and the crack was wide enough for me to see through, and down under me was sharks and swordfishes and other horrible water creatures, which I had never seen before, all driven into the bay, I haven't a doubt, by the violence of the storm out at sea. The thought of my bein' upset and fallin' in among those monsters made my very blood run cold, and involuntary-like I began to turn the handle of the rudder, and in a moment I shot into a wall of ragin' sea-water that was towerin' around me. For a second I was fairly blinded and stunned, but I had the cork out of that oil-can in no time, and very soon—you'd scarcely believe it if I told you how soon—I had another placid mill-pond surroundin' of me. I sat there a-pantin' and fannin' with my straw hat, for you'd better believe I was flustered, and then I began to think how long it would take me to make a line of mill-ponds clean across the head of the bay, and how much oil it would need, and whether I had enough. So I sat and calculated that if a tumblerful of oil would make a smooth place about seven yards across, which I should say was the width of the one I was in,—which I calculated by a measure of my eye as to how many breadths of carpet it would take to cover it,—and if the bay was two miles across betwixt our house and my sister-in-law's, and, although I couldn't get the thing down to exact figures, I saw pretty soon that I wouldn't have oil enough to make a level cuttin' through all those mountainous billows, and besides, even if I had enough to take me across, what would be the good of goin' if there wasn't any oil left to fill my sister-in-law's lamp?

"While I was thinkin' and calculatin' a perfectly dreadful thing happened, which made me think if I didn't get out of this pretty soon I'd find myself in a mighty risky predicament. The oil-can, which I had forgotten to put the cork in, toppled over, and before I could grab it every drop of the oil ran into the hind part of the boat, where it was soaked up by a lot of dry dust that was there. No wonder my heart sank when I saw this. Glancin' wildly around me, as people will do when they are scared, I saw the smooth place I was in gettin' smaller and smaller, for the kerosene was evaporatin', as it will do even off woolen clothes if you give it time enough. The first pond I had come out of seemed to be covered up, and the great, towerin', throbbin' precipice of sea-water was a closin' around me.

"Castin' down my eyes in despair, I happened to look through the crack in the bottom of the boat, and oh, what a blessed relief it was! for down there everything was smooth and still, and I could see the sand on the bottom, as level and hard, no doubt, as it was on the beach. Suddenly the thought struck me that that bottom would give me the only chance I had of gettin' out of the frightful fix I was in. If I could fill that oil-can with air, and then puttin' it under my arm and takin' a long breath if I could drop down on that smooth bottom, I might run along toward shore, as far as I could, and then, when I felt my breath was givin' out, I could take a pull at the oil-can and take another run, and then take another pull and another run, and perhaps the can would hold air enough for me until I got near enough to shore to wade to dry land. To be sure, the sharks and other monsters were down there, but then they must have been awfully frightened, and perhaps they might not remember that man was their nat'ral enemy. Anyway, I thought it would be better to try the smooth water passage down there than stay and be swallowed up by the ragin' waves on top.

"So I blew the can full of air and corked it, and then I tore up some of the boards from the bottom of the boat so as to make a hole big enough for me to get through,—and you sailormen needn't wriggle so when I say that, for you all know a divin'-bell hasn't any bottom at all and the water never comes in,—and so when I got the hole big enough I took the oil-can under my arm, and was just about to slip down through it when I saw an awful turtle a-walkin' through the sand at the bottom. Now, I might trust sharks and swordfishes and sea-serpents to be frightened and forget about their nat'ral enemies, but I never could trust a gray turtle as big as a cart, with a black neck a yard long, with yellow bags to its jaws, to forget anything or to remember anything. I'd as lieve get into a bathtub with a live crab as to go down there. It wasn't of no use even so much as thinkin' of it, so I gave up that plan and didn't once look through that hole again."

"And what did you do, madam?" asked Captain Bird, who was regarding her with a face of stone.

"I used electricity," she said. "Now don't start as if you had a shock of it. That's what I used. When I was younger than I was then, and sometimes visited friends in the city, we often amused ourselves by rubbing our feet on the carpet until we got ourselves so full of electricity that we could put up our fingers and light the gas. So I said to myself that if I could get full of electricity for the purpose of lightin' the gas I could get full of it for other purposes, and so, without losin' a moment, I set to work. I stood up on one of the seats, which was dry, and I rubbed the bottoms of my shoes backward and forward on it with such violence and swiftness that they pretty soon got warm and I began fillin' with electricity, and when I was fully charged with it from my toes to the top of my head, I just sprang into the water and swam ashore. Of course I couldn't sink, bein' full of electricity."

Captain Bird heaved a long sigh and rose to his feet, whereupon the other mariners rose to their feet.

"Madam," said Captain Bird, "what's to pay for the supper and—the rest of the entertainment?"

"The supper is twenty-five cents apiece," said the Widow Ducket, "and everything else is free, gratis."

Whereupon each mariner put his hand into his trousers pocket, pulled out a silver quarter, and handed it to the widow. Then, with four solemn "Good evenin's," they went out to the front gate.

"Cast off, Captain Jenkinson," said Captain Bird, "and you, Captain Burress, clew him up for'ard. You can stay in the bow, Captain Sanderson, and take the sheet-lines. I'll go aft."

All being ready, each of the elderly mariners clambered over a wheel, and having seated themselves, they prepared to lay their course for Cuppertown.

But just as they were about to start, Captain Jenkinson asked that they lay to a bit, and clambering down over his wheel, he reentered the front gate and went up to the door of the house, where the widow and Dorcas were still standing.

"Madam," said he, "I just came back to ask what became of your brother-in-law through his wife's not bein' able to put no light in the window?"

"The storm drove him ashore on our side of the bay," said she, "and the next mornin' he came up to our house, and I told him all that had happened to me. And when he took our boat and went home and told that story to his wife, she just packed up and went out West, and got divorced from him. And it served him right, too."

"Thank you, ma'am," said Captain Jenkinson, and going out of the gate, he clambered up over the wheel, and the wagon cleared for Cuppertown.

When the elderly mariners were gone, the Widow Ducket, still standing in the door, turned to Dorcas.

"Think of it!" she said. "To tell all that to me, in my own house! And after I had opened my one jar of brandied peaches, that I'd been keepin' for special company!"

"In your own house!" ejaculated Dorcas. "And not one of them brandied peaches left!"

The widow jingled the four quarters in her hand before she slipped them into her pocket.

"Anyway, Dorcas," she remarked, "I think we can now say we are square with all the world, and so let's go in and wash the dishes."

"Yes," said Dorcas, "we're square."

A LITTLE MATTER OF REAL ESTATE

BY MYRA KELLY

A LITTLE MATTER OF REAL ESTATE

BY MYRA KELLY

IN AN East Side schoolroom, fifty-six little children of Israel received instruction from an adored young teacher. "Teacher" was the title they had given her, and they knew her by no other. It was Teacher's ambition to give moral tone to her flock, and under her instructions Room 18 became the admiration of the public, to Teacher's vainglorious satisfaction. But pride goes before a fall: and in the third month of her reign of love she was troubled and heavy of heart when it was borne in upon her that two of her little flock—cousins to boot—had so far forgotten the Golden Rule as to be "mad on theirselves und wouldn't to talk even," as that Bureau of Fashionable Intelligence, Sarah Schrodsky, duly reported.

"Und, Teacher," Sarah continued, "Eva Gonorowsky's mama has had a mad on Sarah Gonorowsky's mama, und her papa has had a mad on her papa, und her gran'ma has a mad on both of papas und both of mamas, und her gran'pa has a mad somethin' fierce on both of uncles, und her auntie—"

Teacher sent the too communicative Sarah to her place and called the two members of the divided houses of Gonorowsky to the desk for instant judgment. As she spoke she was delighted to see that her words were falling on good ground, for the dark and dainty features of her hearers expressed a flattering degree of conviction and humility. As she studied the wonderful lashes lying damp and dark on Eva's smooth cheek, the beautiful eyes unclosed, gazed straight across the desk at Sadie, and then Eva took a flying leap into the Teacher's lap, and clung with arms and knees and fingers to her chosen refuge.

"Oh, Teacher, Teacher," she wailed, "Sadie makes on me such a snoot I got a scare over it."

Teacher turned to the so lately placid face of Sadie in search of the devastating "snoot," but met only a serene glance of conscious guilelessness and the assurance:

"No, ma'an, I don't makes no snoot on nobody. I get killed as anything off my mama so I makes a snoot. It ain't polite." This with a reassuring smile and a direct and candid gaze.

"Teacher, yiss ma'an, she makes all times a snoot on me," cried the now weeping Eva, "all times. She turns her nose around, und she makes go away her eyes, und comes her tongue out long. Only I dassn't to fight mit her while I'm cousins mit her. Und over cousins you got all times kind feelings."

"Well, Sadie," Teacher questioned, "what have you to say?"

The dark eyes met Teacher's with no shadow in their depths as Sadie uttered her denial:

"I *never* in my world done no snoot."

A shudder of admiring awe swept over the assembled class—followed by a gasp of open contradiction as Sadie went on with her vindication, for Sadie's snoots were the envy of all the class. Had not Morris Mogilewsky paid three cents for lessons in the art, and, with the result, frightened a baby into what an angry mother described as "spinyell convulsions"? And now Sadie was saying, "I *couldn't* to make no snoot, never. But, Teacher, it's like this: Eva makes *me* whole bunches of trouble; Julia und me is monitors in the yard when the children comes back from dinner. So-ooh I says, 'front dress' like you says, so the children shall look on what head is in front of them. Only Eva she don't 'front dress' at all, but extra she longs out her neck und rubs on me somethin' fierce—"

"It's a lie!" interrupted Eva gently. "I don't make nothing like that. I stands by my line und Sadie she makes faces on me with her hand. It ain't polite." This with plaintive self-righteousness. "No, ma'an, it *ain't* polite—you make snoots mit your hand like this." Here Eva illustrated with outspread fingers and pink thumb in juxtaposition to a diminutive nose, and Teacher with uncertain gravity was forced to admit that snoots of that description are sanctioned by few books of etiquette.

"Now, my dear little girls," said Teacher, "this quarreling must stop. I think you ought to kiss each other as cousins should."

This suggestion was a distinct failure. Eva and Sadie, with much fluttering of aprons and waving of curls, sought opposite corners of the schoolroom, while up started Sarah Schrodsky: "Teacher, they couldn't to make no kissing. They're mad on themselves cause their mamas had a fight. Sadie's mama says like this to Eva's mama—'Don't you dast to talk to me—you lives by the fifth floor already, und your man is a robber.' Und Eva's mama says—"

When Teacher had managed to silence Sarah she led the weeping Gonorowskys back to their places. And the scholastic world wagged on in outward tranquillity.

Hostilities were temporarily suspended owing to the illness of Sadie, by far the more aggressive of the opposing parties. Eva led a placid life for three peaceful days, and then—as by law prescribed—invited by postal card, Sadie's mother came to explain her daughter's absence. Large, bland of manner, in a heavy black shawl and a heavier black wig, Mrs. Lazarus Gonorowsky stood beaming and bobbing in the hall.

"I like I should Sadie Gonorowsky's teacher see," she began, in the peculiar English of the adult population of the East Side. Mrs. Gonorowsky could neither use nor understand her young daughter's copious invective. Upon being assured that the diminutive form before her was indeed clothed with authority, she announced:

"Comes a letter I should by the school come. I was Sadie's mama." Here she drew from the inner recesses of the black shawl a bundle which, being placed in a perpendicular position, proved to be the most recent addition to the Gonorowsky household. She smoothed the bundle with a work-worn but tender hand and repeated with saddened voice: "Yes, ma'am, I was her mama und she lies now on the bed."

The increasing sadness in Mrs. Gonorowsky's voice and the sinister phraseology startled Teacher.

"Not dead!" she cried. "Oh, surely not dead!"

"Sure not," was the indignant response. "She's got such a sickness she must lay on the bed, und comes the Doctor. Sadie's papa holds much on that child, Miss Teacher, und all times he has a worry over her—me too. She come by the school to-morrow maybe, und I ask you by a favor you should do me the kindness to look on her. So she feel again sick she should better on the house come. She say, 'Oh, mama, I got a lovely teacher; I likes to look on her the while she has such a light face.'"

Having thus diplomatically led up to the question, Mrs. Gonorowsky with great suavity asked, "Sadie is a good girl, hein?"

"Oh, yes, indeed."

"She is shmardt, hein? She don't make you no trouble?"

"Well," answered Teacher, "she has rather bothered me lately by quarreling with her cousin, Eva Gonorowsky."

"So-ooh!" exclaimed Sadie's parent ponderously. "So-ooh, Eva makes you trouble; she is a most bad girl—I tell Sadie—Sadie is a good girl—I tell her she should make nothing with Eva, soch a bad girl. For what you not put her back to baby class? She is not shmardt."

"Oh, but she is; she is a bright little thing," cried Teacher. "I couldn't think of putting her back. She's a dear little girl. I can't imagine why Sadie quarrels with her."

Mrs. Gonorowsky drew her ample form to a wonderful erectness as she adjusted her shawl, and answered with much stateliness:

"It was a trouble off of real estate." With dignity

and blandness she then kissed Teacher's hand and signified entire willingness to entrust her precious Sadie to the care of so estimable a young person, inquired solicitously if the work were not too much for so small a lady, and cautioned the young person against rainy mornings. Had she a mackintosh? Mr. Gonorowsky was selling them off that week. Were her imperceptibles sufficiently warm? Mr. Gonorowsky, by a strange chance, was absolutely giving away "fine all from wool" imperceptibles, and the store was near. Mrs. Gonorowsky then withdrew, leaving a kindly sentiment in Teacher's heart and an atmosphere of ironing-boards and onions in the hall. On the following morning Sadie returned to her light-faced teacher, and for one whole day hostilities were suspended.

On the morning after this truce Eva was absent from her accustomed place, and Sadie blandly disclaimed all knowledge of her whereabouts. After the noon recess a pathetic little figure wavered in the doorway of the schoolroom with one arm in a sling and one eye in a poultice. The remaining eye was fixed in deep reproach on the face of Isidore Belchatosky, the Adonis of the class, and the eye was the eye of Eva.

"Eva!" exclaimed Teacher, "oh, Eva, what can you have been doing? What's the matter with your eye?"

"Isidore Belchatosky he goes und makes me in this here shiner," said Eva's accusing voice, as the eye under the poultice was uncovered for a moment. It was indeed a shiner of aggravated aspect, and Isidore cringed as it met his affrighted gaze. The sling and the bandages were of gay chintz, showing forth the adventures of Robinson Crusoe, and their lurid colors made them horribly conspicuous. Friday scampered across Eva's forehead, pursued by savages, and Crusoe, under his enormous umbrella, nestled close to her heart.

"Surely Isidore would never hit a little girl?" Teacher remonstrated.

"Teacher, yiss, ma'an; he makes me this here shiner. Sadie she goes und tells him, she kisses him a kiss so he makes me a shiner. He's lovin' mit her und she's got kind feelin's by him, the while his papa keeps a candy cart. It's a stylish candy cart mit a bell und a horn. So I was yesterday for buy my mama some wurst, und I don't make nothin' mit nobody."

Here the poor half-blind Eva, with her love and talent for pantomime, took a gay little walk past Teacher's desk, tossing her head and swinging her skirts. Then with a cry she recoiled from the very memory of her wrongs.

"Come Isidore! Und he hits me a hack on my leg so I couldn't to hold it even. So I falls und I make me this here shiner. Und when my mama seen how comes such a bile on my bone she had a mad; she hollered somethin' fierce."

One could well sympathize with the harassed Mrs. Nathan Gonorowsky.

"So," continued Eva with melancholy enjoyment, "my mama she puts medsin at a rag und bandages up mine eye. Und now I ain't healthy."

Teacher forgot moral tone and the ethical ascendancy of Room 18, for she was savagely angry.

"Sadie!" she called, "and Isidore! Come here."

Teacher strove dutifully to remember the by-laws forbidding corporal punishment. Then with long strange words to supply the element of dread uncertainty Teacher began to speak: slowly and coldly as one should when addressing ears accustomed to much sputtering profanity.

"Sadie and Isidore, did you dare to interfere with the life, the liberty, and the happiness of your cherished young friend, Eva Gonorowsky? Did you dare?"

"No, ma'an," said Sadie with a sob.

"It's a lie!" said Isidore with a snuffle.

"Did you, Isidore, allow yourself to be tempted by beauty to such inconceivable depravity as to blacken Eva's eye?"

"No, ma'an. Self done it."

"Did you, Sadie, descend so low as to barter kisses with Isidore Belchatosky?"

"No, ma'an," this with much scorn. "I wouldn't to kiss him; he's a scare-cat, und he tells out."

"What did he tell?" asked Teacher.

"He tells out how I say I kiss him a kiss so he make Eva a shiner. Und I wouldn't to do it. Never. So he gave me five cents even I wouldn't to kiss no scare-cat."

"Well, then, why did you promise?"

"'Cause I couldn't hit her mineself," said the doughty Sadie. She was inches taller than her victim, and stout withal. "I couldn't 'cause I ain't so healthy; I'm a nervous child, Teacher, und I was day-before-yesterday sick on the bed."

Here the plaintiff showed a desire to testify once more, and Teacher appointed three-thirty as the hour most suitable for a thorough examination of the case.

When the last arm had been twisted into the last sleeve, when the last chin had been tied into the last shawl, when the last dispute as to ownership in disreputable mittens had been settled, the great case of Gonorowsky vs. Gonorowsky was called. On either side of the desk stood a diminutive Gonorowsky; Eva still plaintive, and Sadie redly on the defensive. Directly in front stood that laborer defrauded of his hire, that tool in the hands of a guileful woman—Isidore Belchatosky.

"Now," Teacher began, "I intend to find out why you two little girls are disgracing this class and this teacher; I want to hear nothing but the truth. Now, Isidore, did you hit Eva?"

"Yiss, ma'an."

"What for?"

"For a kiss."

"From whom?"

Here Sadie muttered a threat "to lay him down dead if he tells," and Isidore required promise of safe conduct to his own block before he consented to murmur:

"Sadie Gonorowsky."

"Did you get the kiss?"

"No, ma'an."

"Do you know anything about this fight?"

"No, ma'an."

"Well, then, you may go home now, and bring your mother with you to-morrow morning."

"When she sees this shiner she will have a mad," Eva volunteered, as she once more uncovered the eye and turned its dreadful rainbow hues upon the culprits.

"Patrick Brennan's papa could arrest you—think shame."

Isidore left with a heavy heart and the inquiry was continued.

"What has Sadie been doing to you, Eva?" asked Teacher, and Eva with resigned mien began.

"All things," and then details followed. "She makes on me a snoot, she pulls me on the bottom of my hair, she goes und takes her pencil und gives me a stick in my face. When I was marchin' she extra takes her shoes und steps at my legs; I got two swollen legs over her. Und now"—here a sob—"you could to look on how she makes me biles und shiners."

As Eva's voice droned out these many accusations, Sadie grew more emphatic in her favorite repartee:

"It's a lie! It's a lie! It's a lie!"

"And now, Eva, will you tell me *why* Sadie has been doing all these naughty things?"

"Teacher, I don't know."

"Oh, yes; you do!"

"No, ma'an; I don't. I could swear if I do. I kiss up to God." She wafted a kiss toward the ceiling. "I got all times a kind feelin' over Sadie, on'y she wouldn't to be glad on me. I seen yesterday her little brother in the street mit Sadie und she make he shouldn't to talk to me. My heart it breaks when she make like that; I'm got no brother und no sister und I'm lovin' so much mit my little cousin. She goes und makes he should say nothin' und in my eyes stands tears. I was sad."

"Well, dear, that's a shame," said Teacher, "and if you really don't understand go out into the assembly room and wait for me. Sadie is going to tell me all about it."

Eva vanished only to return with the lurid bandage in her hand and the query:—"Can I make this wet?"

Upon receiving permission so to do she retired with her courteous "Good afternoon, Teacher," and her unchanged "Good by, Sadie; I've got yet that kind feelin'." Truly the "pangs of disprized love" seemed hers.

Several kinds of persuasion were practised in Room 18 during the next five minutes. Then Sadie accepted defeat, faced the inevitable, and began:

"It's like this: I dassn't to be glad on Eva. So I want even, I dassn't. My mama has the same mad, und my papa. My mama she says like this. So my papa gets sooner glad on my uncle she wouldn't to be wifes mit him no more! *Such* is the mad she has!"

"Why?"

"Well. My uncle he come out of Russia. From long he come when I was a little bit of baby und he didn't to have no money for buy a house. So my papa—he's awful kind—he gives him thousen dollers so he could to buy. Und say, Teacher, what you think? he don't pays it back. It *ain't* polite you takes thousen dollers und don't pay it back."

Sadie's air as she submitted this rule of social etiquette to Teacher's wider knowledge was a wondrous thing to see—so deferential was it, and yet so assured.

"So my papa he writes a letter on my uncle how he could to pay that thousen dollers. *Goes* months. *Comes* no thousen dollers. So my papa he goes on the lawyer und the lawyer he writes on my uncle a letter how he should to pay. *Goes* months. *Comes* no thousen dollers." At each repetition of these fateful words Sadie shook her serious head, pursed up her rosy mouth, folded her hands resignedly across a flat little stomach, and sighed deeply. Clearly this was a tale more than twice told, for the voice and manner of Sadie were as the voice and manner of Mrs. Lazarus Gonorowsky, and the recital was plagiarism—masterly and complete.

"And then?" prompted Teacher, lest the conversation languish.

"Well, my papa he writes again on my uncle a awful bossy letter. My uncle must have a mad when he seen how my papa write. *Goes* two days. *Comes* no thousen dollers."

Here ensued a long and dramatic pause.

"Well, comes no thousen dollers. Comes nothing. On'y by night my mama she puts me on my bed; when comes my uncle! He come, und make a knopping on our door. I couldn't to tell even how he makes knopping. I had such a scare, I was green on the face, und my heart was going so you could to hear. I'm a nervous child, Teacher, und my face is all times green sooner I get a scare."

This last observation was a triumph of mimicry, and recalled Mrs. Gonorowsky so vividly as to make her atmosphere of garlic and old furniture quite perceptible.

"So my mama hears how my uncle knopps und

says 'Lemme in—lemme in.' She says ('scuse me, Teacher)—she says 'he must be' (scuse me) 'drunk.' That's how my mama says.

"So goes my papa by the door und says 'Who stands?' Und my uncle he says 'Lemme in.' So-ooh my papa he opens the door. Stands my uncle mit cheeky look und he showed a fist on my papa. My papa had a fierce mad sooner he seen that fist—fists is awful cheeky when somebody ain't paid. So my papa he says ('scuse me)—it's awful how he says on'y he had a mad over that fist. He says ('scuse me), 'Go to hell!' und my uncle, what ain't paid that thousen dollers, he says just like to my papa. He says too ('scuse me, Teacher), 'Go to hell!' So-ooh then my papa hits my uncle (that's Eva's papa), und how my papa is strong I couldn't to tell even. He pulls every morning by the extrasizer, und he's got such a muscles. So he hits my uncle (that's Eva's papa), und my uncle he fall und he fall und he fall—we live by the third floor—und even in falling he says like that ('scuse me, Teacher), 'Go to hell! go to hell!' It fierce, on'y but that's how he says. On all the steps he says 'Go to hell! go to hell! go to hell!' ('scuse me)."

Teacher appreciated the futility of interference in a family feud, so she contented herself with keeping a watchful eye on Sadie and tying Eva to the side of the throne where violence was impossible during school hours. Sadie was warned that on the first appearance of evil she would be delivered into the hands of the Board of Health.

Some weeks later Eva was again missing, and

Sadie presented the explanation in a rather dirty envelope.

"Dear Miss:

"Excuse pliss that Eva Gonorowsky comes not on the school. We was moving un she couldn't to find her clothes. Yurs Resptphs,

"Her elders,

"NATHAN GONOROWSKY,

"BECKY GANURWOSKI."

"Is Eva going far away?" asked Teacher. "Will she come to this school any more?"

"Teacher, yiss, ma'an, sure she comes; she lives now by my house. My uncle he lives by my house, too. Und my aunt."

"And you're not angry with your cousin any more?"

"Teacher, no, ma'an; I'm loving mit her. She's got on now all mine best clothes the while her mama buys her new. My aunt buys new clothes, too. Und my uncle."

Sadie reported this shopping epidemic so cheerfully that Teacher asked with mild surprise:

"Where are all their old things?"

"Teacher, they're burned. Und my uncle's store und his *all* of goods, und his house, und his three sewing machines. All, all burned!"

"Oh, dear me!" said Teacher. "Your poor uncle. Now he can never pay that thousand dollars."

Sadie regarded Teacher with puzzled eyes.

"Sure he pays. He's now most as rich like Van'bilt. He pays all right, und my papa had a party over him, he had such an awful glad."

"Glad on your uncle?" cried Teacher, startled into colloquialisms.

"Yiss, ma'an. Und my mama has a glad on Eva's mama, und my gran'ma has a glad on both of papas und both of mamas, und my gran'pa has a glad just like my gran'ma. All, all glad."

As Teacher walked toward Grand street that afternoon, she met a radiant little girl with a small and most unsteady boy in tow. She recognized Eva and surmised the cousin whose coldness had hurt her even unto tears.

"Well, Eva, what little boy is this?" she asked.

And the beaming and transformed Eva answered:

"It's my little cousin. He's lovin' mit me now. Sadie, too, is lovin'. I take him out the while, it's healthy he walks, on'y he ain't so big und he falls. Say, Teacher, it's nice when he falls. I hold him in my hands."

And fall he did. Eva picked him up, greatly to their mutual delight, and explained:

"He's heavy, und my this here arm ain't yet so healthy, but I hold him in my hands the while he's cousins mit me, und over cousins I'm got all times that kind feelin'."

THE ESCAPE OF WILKINS

BY ARTHUR TRAIN

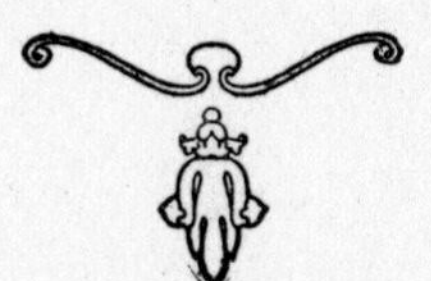

THE ESCAPE OF WILKINS

BY ARTHUR TRAIN

I

"PARTY to see you, sir, in the visitors' room. Didn't have a card. Said you would know him, sir."

Although Peter spoke in his customary deferential tones there was a queer look upon his face that did not escape McAllister as the latter glanced up from the afternoon paper which he had been perusing in the window.

"H'm!" remarked the clubman, gazing out at the rain falling in torrents. Who in thunder could be calling upon him a day like this, when there wasn't even a cab in sight and the policemen had sought sanctuary in convenient vestibules. It was evident that this "party" must want to see him very badly indeed.

"What shall I say, sir?" continued Peter gently.

McAllister glanced sharply at him. Of course it was absurd to suppose that Peter, or any one else, had heard of the extraordinary events at the Blairs' the night before; of the theft of the Benson pearls, the escape of the burglar in McAllister's coat and hat under the very nose of the best detective on the New York police, and the clubman's own part in the transaction, during which he had not only recovered the famous jewels but had also connived at the escape of the criminal—his old valet, Wilkins. No, Peter could know nothing of them, yet vaguely McAllister felt that this stranger must in some mysterious way be connected with the occurrences referred to. In any case there was no use trying to duck the consequences of the adventure, whatever they might prove to be.

"I'll see him," said the clubman. Maybe it was another detective after additional information, or perhaps a reporter. Without hesitation he crossed the marble hall and parted the portières of the visitors' room. Before him stood the rain-soaked, bedraggled figure of the valet.

"Wilkins!" he gasped.

The burglar raised his head and disclosed a countenance haggard from the lack of sleep, and the strain of the pursuit. Little rivers of rain streamed from his cuffs, his (McAllister's) coat-tails, and from the brim of his master's hat, which he held deprecatingly before him. There was a look of fear in his eyes and he trembled like a hare which pauses uncertain in which direction to escape.

"Forgive me, sir! Oh, sir, forgive me! They're right hafter me! Just houtside, sir! It was my honly chance!"

McAllister gazed at him horrified and speechless.

"You see, sir," continued Wilkins in accents of breathless terror, "I caught the train last night and reached the city a'ead of the detective. I knew 'e'd 'ave telegraphed a general halarm, so I 'id in a harea all night. This mornin' I thought I'd given 'im the slip, but I walked square into 'im on Fiftieth Street.

I took it on a run hup Sixth Havenue, doubled 'round a truck, an' thought I'd lost 'im, but 'e saw me on Fifty-third Street an' started dead after me. I think 'e saw me stop in 'ere, sir. Wot shall I do, sir? You won't give me hup, will you, sir?"

Before McAllister could reply there was a commotion at the door of the club, and he recognized the clear tones of Barney Conville.

"Who am I? I'm a sergeant of police—Detective Bureau. You've just passed in a burglar! He must be right inside. Let me in, I say."

Wilkins shrank back toward the curtains.

There was a slight scuffle, but the servant outside placed his foot behind the door in such a position that the detective could not enter. Then Peter came to the rescue.

"What do you mean by tryin' to force your way into a private club, like this? I'll telephone the inspector. Get out of here, now! Get away from that door!"

"Inspector nothin'! Let me in!"

"Have you got a warrant?"

The question seemed to stagger the detective for a moment and his adversary seized the opportunity to close the door. Then Peter knocked politely upon the other side of the curtains.

"I'm afraid, Mr. McAllister, I can't keep the officer out much longer. It's only a question of time. You'll pardon me, sir?"

"Of course, Peter," answered McAllister.

He stepped to the window. Outside he could see Conville stationing two plainclothes men so as to guard both exits from the club. McAllister's breath came fast. Wilkins crouched in terror by the center-table. Then a momentary inspiration came to the clubman.

"Er—Peter! This is my friend, Mr. Lloyd-Jones. Take his coat and hat, give me a check for them, and then show him upstairs to a room. He'll be here for an hour or so."

"Very good, sir," replied Peter without emotion, as he removed Wilkins's dripping coat and hat. "This way, sir."

Casting a look of dazed gratitude at his former master, the valet followed Peter toward the elevator.

"Here's a nice mess!" thought McAllister, as he returned to the big room. "How am I ever goin' to get rid of him? And ain't I liable somehow as an accomplice?"

He wrinkled his brows, lit a Perfecto, and sank again into his accustomed place by the window.

"That policeman wants to see you, sir," said the doorman, suddenly appearing at his elbow. "Says he knows you, and it's somethin' very important."

The clubman smothered a curse. His first impulse was to tell the impudent fellow to go to the devil, but then he thought better of it. He had beaten Conville once, and he would do so again. When it came to a show-down he reckoned his brains were about as good as a policeman's.

"All right," he replied. "Tell him to sit down;—that I've just come in, and will be with him in a few moments."

"Very good, sir," answered the servant.

McAllister perceived that he must think rapidly. There was no escape from the conclusion that he was certainly assisting in the escape of a felon; that he was an accessory after the fact, as it were. The idea did not increase his happiness at all. His one experience in the Tombs, however adventitious, had been quite sufficient. Nevertheless, he could not go back on Wilkins, particularly now that he had promised to assist him. McAllister rubbed his broad forehead in perplexity.

"The officer says he's in a great hurry, sir, and wants to know can you see him at once, sir," said the doorman, coming back.

"Hang it!" exclaimed our hero. "Yes, I'll *see* him."

He got up and walked slowly to the visitors' room again, while Peter, with a studiously unconscious expression, held the portières open. He entered, prepared for the worst. As he did so, Conville sprang to his feet, leaving a pool of water in front of the sofa and tossing little drops of rain from the ends of his mustache.

"Look here, Mr. McAllister. There's been enough of this. Where's Welch, the crook who ran in here a few moments ago? Oh, he's here fast enough. I've got your club covered, front and behind. Don't try to 'con' *me*."

McAllister slowly adjusted his monocle, smiled affably, and sank comfortably into an armchair.

"Why, it's you, Baron, isn't it! How are you? Won't you have a little nip of somethin' warm? No? A cigar, then. Here, Peter, bring the gentleman an Obsequio. Well, to what do I owe this honor?"

Conville glared at him enraged. However, he restrained his wrath. A wise detective never puts himself at a disadvantage by giving way to useless emotion. When Peter returned with the cigar, Barney took it mechanically and struck a match, meanwhile keeping one eye upon the door of the club.

"I suppose," he presently remarked, "you think you're smart. Well, you're mistaken. I had you wrong last night, I admit—that is, so far as your identity was concerned. You're a real high roller, all right, but that ain't the whole thing by a long shot. How would you like to wander down to headquarters as an accomplice?"

A few chills played hide and seek around the base of the clubman's spine.

"Don't be an ass!" he finally managed to ejaculate.

"Oh, I can't connect you with the necklace. You're safe enough there," Barney continued. "But how about this little game right here in this club? You're aiding in the escape of a felon. That's *felony*. You know that yourself. Besides, when you locked me in the bathroom last night you assaulted an officer in the performance of his duty. I've got you dead to rights, *see?*"

McAllister laughed lightly.

"By jiminy," he exclaimed. "I *thought* you were crazy all the time, and now I *know* it. What in thunder are you driving at?"

Conville knocked the ashes off his cigar impatiently.

"Drivin' at? Drivin' at? Where's Welch?—Fatty Welch, that ran in here five minutes ago?"

McAllister assumed a puzzled expression.

"Welch? No one ran in here except myself. *I* came in about that time. Got off the L at Fiftieth Street, footed it pretty fast up Sixth Avenue, and then through Fifty-third Street to the club. I got mighty well wet, too, I tell you!"

"Don't think you can throw that game into *me!*" shouted Conville. "You can't catch me twice *that* way. It was *Welch* I saw, not you."

"You don't believe me?"

McAllister pressed the bell and Peter entered.

"Peter, tell this gentleman how many persons have come into the club within the hour."

"Why, only *you,* sir," replied Peter, without hesitation. "Your clothes was wringin' wet, sir. No one else has entered the club since twelve o'clock."

"Bah!" exclaimed Conville. "If it was *you* that came in," he added cunningly, "suppose you show me the check and let me have a look at your coat!"

"Certainly," responded McAllister, beginning to regain his equanimity, as he drew Wilkins's check from his pocket. "Here it is. You can step over and get the coat for yourself."

Barney seized the small square of brass, crossed to the coat-room, and returned with the dripping garment, which he held up to the light at the window.

"You ought to find Poole's name under the collar, and my own inside the breastpocket," remarked "Chubby" encouragingly. "It's there, isn't it?"

Conville threw the soaked object over a chair-back and made a rapid inspection, then turned to McAllister with an expression of bewilderment.

"I—you—how—" he stammered.

"Don't you remember," laughed his tormentor, "that there was a big truck on the corner as I turned into Fifty-third Street?"

Barney set his teeth.

"I see you *do,*" continued McAllister. "Well, what

more can I do for you? Are you sure you won't have that drink?"

But Conville was in no mood for drinking. Stepping up to the clubman, he looked searchingly down into his face.

"Mr. McAllister," he hissed, "you think you've got me criss-crossed. You think you're a sure winner. But I *know* you. I know your *face*. And this time I don't lose you, *see?* You're in cahoots with Welch. You're his side-partner. You'll see me again. Remember, you're a *common felon*."

The detective made for the door.

"Don't say 'common,'" murmured McAllister, as Conville disappeared. Then his nonchalant look gave place to one of extreme dejection. "Peter," he gasped, "tell Mr. Lloyd-Jones I must see him at once."

Peter soon returned with the unexpected information that "Mr. Lloyd-Jones" had gone to bed and wouldn't get up.

"Says he's sick, sir," said Peter, trying hard to retain his gravity.

McAllister made one jump for the elevator. Peter followed. Of course, *he* had known Wilkins when the latter was in McAllister's employ.

"I put him in Number Thirteen, sir," remarked the majordomo.

Sure enough, Wilkins was in bed. His clothes were nowhere visible and the quilt was pulled well up around his fat neck. He seemed utterly to have lost his nerve.

"Oh, sir," he cried apologetically, "I was hafraid to come down, sir. *Without my clothes* they never could hidentify me, sir!"

"What on earth have you done with 'em?" cried his master.

"Oh, Mr. McAllister," wailed Wilkins, "I couldn't think o' nothin' else, so I just threw 'em hout the window, into the hair-shaft."

At this intelligence Peter, who had lingered by the door, choked violently and retired down the hall.

"Wilkins," exclaimed McAllister, "I never took you for a fool before. Pray what do you propose to do now?"

"I don't know, sir."

"Can't you see what an awkward position you've placed me in?" went on McAllister. "I'm liable for arrest for aiding in your escape. In fact, that detective has just threatened to take me to headquarters."

"'Oly Moses!" moaned Wilkins. "Oh, wot shall I do! If you only get me haway, sir, I promise you I'll never return."

McAllister closed the door, sat down by the bed, and puffed hard at his cigar.

"I'll try it!" he muttered at length. "Wilkins, you remember you always wore my clothes."

"Yessir," sighed Wilkins.

"Well, to-night you shall leave the club in my dress-suit, tall hat, and Inverness—understand? You'll take a cab from here at eleven forty. Go to the Grand Central and board the twelve o'clock train for Boston. Here's a ticket and the check for the drawing-room. You'll be Mr. McAllister of the Colophon Club, if any one speaks to you. You're going on to Mr. Cabot's wedding to-morrow, to act as best man. Turn in as soon as you go on board, and don't let any one disturb you. I'll be on the train myself, and after it starts I'll knock three times on the door."

"Very good, sir," murmured Wilkins.

"I'll send to my rooms for the clothes at once. Do you think you can do it?"

"Oh, certainly, sir. Thank you, sir. I'll be there, sir, never fail."

"Well, good luck to you!"

McAllister returned to the big room downstairs. The longer he thought of his plan the better he liked it. He was going to the Winthrops' Twelfth Night party that evening as Henry VIII. He would dress at the club and leave it in costume about nine o'clock. Conville would never recognize him in doublet and hose, and, when Wilkins departed at eleven forty, would in all likelihood take the latter for McAllister. If he could thus get rid of his ex-valet for good and all it would be cheap at twice the trouble. So far as spiriting away Wilkins was concerned the whole thing seemed easy enough, and McAllister, once more in his usual state of genial placidity, ordered as good a dinner as the *chef* could provide.

II

The revelry was at its height when Henry VIII realized with a start that it was already half after eleven. First there had been a professional presentation of the scene between Sir Andrew Aguecheek and Sir Toby Belch that had made McAllister shake with merriment. He thought Sir Andrew the drollest fellow that he had seen for many a day. Maria and the clown were both good, too. McAllister had a fleeting wish that he had essayed Sir Toby. The champagne had been excellent and the characters most amusing, and altogether, McAllister did not blame himself for having overstayed his time—in fact, he didn't care much whether he had or not. He had intended going back to his rooms for the purpose of changing his costume, but he had plenty of clothes on the train and there really seemed no need of it at all. He bade his hostess good night in a most optimistic frame of mind and hailed a cab. The long ulster which he wore entirely concealed his costume save for his shoes, strange creations of undressed leather, red on the uppers and white between the toes. As for his cap and feather, he was quite too happy to mind them for an instant. The assembled crowd of lackeys and footmen cheered him mildly as he drove away, but Henry VIII, smoking a large cigar, noticed them not. Neither did he observe a slim young man who darted out from behind a flight of steps and followed the cab, keeping about half a block in the rear. The rain had stopped. The clouds had drawn aside their curtains, and a big friendly moon beamed down on McAllister from an azure sky, bright almost as day.

The cabman hit up his pace as they reached the slope from the Cathedral down Fifth Avenue and the runner was distanced by several blocks. McAllister, happy and sleepy, was blissfully unconscious of being an actor in a drama of vast import to the New York police, but as they reached Forty-third Street he saw by the illuminated clock upon the Grand Central Station that it was two minutes to twelve. At the same moment a trace broke. The driver sprang from his seat, but before he could reach the ground McAllister had leaped out. Tossing a bill to the perturbed cabby, our hero threw off his ulster and sped with an agility marvelous to behold down Forty-third Street toward the station. As he dashed across Madison Avenue, directly in front of an electric car, the hand on the clock slipped a minute nearer. At that instant the slim man turned the corner from Fifth Avenue and redoubled his speed.

Thirty seconds later McAllister, in sword, doublet, hose, and feathered cap, burst into the waiting-room, carrying an ulster, cleared half its length in six strides threw himself through the revolving door to the platform, and sprang past the astonished gateman just as he was sliding-to the gate.

"Hi, there, give us yer ticket!" yelled that official after the retreating form of Henry VIII, but royalty made no response.

The gate closed, a gong rang twice, somewhere up ahead an engine gave half a dozen spasmodic coughs, and the forward section of the train began to pull out.

McAllister, gasping for breath, a terrible pain in his side, his ulster seeming to weigh a thousand pounds, stumbled upon the platform of the car next the last. As he did so, the slim young man rushed to the gate and commenced to beat frantically upon it. The gateman, indignant, approached to make use of severe language.

"Open this gate!" yelled the man. "There's a burglar on that train in disguise. Didn't you see him run through? Open up!"

"Whata yer givin' us?" answered Gate. "Who are yer, anyhow?"

"I'm a detective sergeant!" shrieked the one outside, excitedly exhibiting a shield. "I order you to open this gate and let me through."

Gate looked with exasperating deliberateness after the receding train; the red lights were just passing out of the station.

"Oh, go to—!" said he through the bars.

"Is this car 2241?" inquired the breathless McAllister at the same moment, as he staggered inside.

"Sho, boss," replied the porter, grinning from ear to ear, as he received the ticket and its accompanying half-dollar. "Drawin' room, sah? Yessah. Right here, sah! Yo' frien', he arrived some time ago. May Ah enquire what personage yo represent, sah? A most magnificent sword, sah!"

"Where's the smoking compartment?" asked McAllister.

"Udder end, sah!"

Now McAllister had no inclination to feel his way the length of that swaying car. He perceived that the smoking compartment of the car behind would naturally be much more convenient.

"I'm goin' into the next car to smoke for awhile," he informed the darky.

No one was in the smoking compartment of the "Benvolio," which was bright and warm, and, McAllister, throwing down his ulster, stretched luxuriously across the cushions, lit a cigar, and watched with interest the myriad lights of the greater city marching past, those near at hand flashing by with the velocity of meteors, and those beyond swinging slowly forward along the outer rim of the circle. And the idea of this huge circle, its circumference ever changing with the forward movement of its pivot, beside which the train was rushing, never passing that mysterious edge which fled before them into infinity, took hold on McAllister's imagination, and he fancied, as he sped onward, that in some mysterious way, if he could only square that circle or calculate its radius, he could solve the problem of existence. What was it he had learned when a boy at St. Timothy's about the circle? Pi R—one—two—two Pi R! That was it! "$2 \pi r$"—"$2 \pi r$."

The smoke from his cigar swirled thickly around the Pintsch light in the ceiling, and Henry VIII, oblivious of the anachronism, with sword and feathered cap upon the sofa beside him, gazed solemnly into space.

"Br—r—clink!—br—r—clink!" went the track.

"Two Pi R!" murmured McAllister." "Two Pi R!"

III

UNDER the big moon's yellow disk, beside and past the roaring train, along the silent reaches of the Sound, leaping on its copper thread from pole to pole, jumping from insulator to insulator, from town to town, sped a message concerning Henry VIII. The night operator at New Haven, dozing over a paper in the corner, heard his call four times before he came to his senses. Then he sent the answer rattling back with a simulation of indignation.

"Yes—yes— What's your rush?"

"Special—Police—Headquarters—New Haven. Escaped ex-convict Welch on No. 13 from New York. Notify McGinnis. In complete disguise. Arrest and notify. Particulars long distance phone in morning.

"EBSTEIN."

The operator crossed the room and unhooked the telephone.

"Headquarters, please."

"Yes. Headquarters! Is McGinnis of the New York Detective Bureau there? Tell him he's wanted to make an important arrest on board No. 13 when she comes through at two-twenty. Sorry. Say, tell him to bring along some cigars. I'll give him the complete message down here."

Then the operator went back to his paper. In a few moments he suddenly sat up.

"By gum!" he ejaculated.

"BOLD ATTEMPT AT BURGLARY IN COUNTRY HOUSE

"It was learned to-day that a well-known crook had been successful recently in securing a position as a servant at Mr. Gordon Blair's, at Scarsdale. Last evening one of the guests missed her valuable pearl necklace. In the excitement which followed the burglar made his escape, leaving the necklace behind him. The perpetrator of this bold attempt is the notorious 'Fatty Welch,' now wanted in several States as a fugitive from justice."

"By gum!" repeated the operator, throwing down the paper. Then he went to the drawer and took out a small bull-dog revolver, which he carefully loaded.

"Br—r—clink!—br—r—clink!" went the track, as the train swung round the curve outside New Haven.

The brakes groaned, the porters waked from troubled slumbers in wicker chairs, one or two old women put out their arms and peered through the window shades, and the train thundered past the depot and slowly came to a full stop. Ahead the engine panted and steamed. Two gnomes ran, Mimi-like, out of a cavernous darkness behind the station and by the light of flaring torches began to hammer and tap the flanges. The conductor, swinging off the rear car, ran into the embrace of a huge Irishman. At the same moment a squad of policemen separated and scattered to the different platforms.

"Here! Let me go!" gasped the conductor. "What's all this?"

"Say, Cap., I'm McGinnis—Central Office, New York. You've got a burglar on board. They're after wirin' me to make the arrest."

"Burglar be damned!" yelled the conductor. "Do you think you can hold me up and search my train? Why, I'd be two hours late!"

"I won't take more'n fifteen minutes," continued McGinnis, making for the rear car.

"Come back there, you!" shouted the conductor, grasping him firmly by the coat-tails. "You can't wake up all the passengers."

"Look here, Cap.," expostulated the detective. "Don't ye see I've got to make this arrest? It won't take a minute. The porters 'll know who they've got, and you're runnin' awful light. Have a good cigar?"

The conductor took the weed so designated and swore loudly. It was the biggest piece of gall on record. Well, hang it, he didn't want to take McGinnis all the way to Boston, and, even if he did, there would be the same confounded mix-up at the other end. He admitted finally that it was a fine night. Did McGinnis want a nip? He had a bottle in the porter's closet. Yes, call out those niggers and make 'em tell what they knew.

The conductor was now just as insistent that the burglar should be arrested then and there as he had been before that the train should not be held up. He rushed through the cars telling the various porters to go outside. Eight or ten presently assembled upon the platform. They filled McGinnis with unspeakable repulsion.

The conductor began with car No. 2204.

"Now, Deacon, who have you got?"

The Deacon, an enormously fat darky, rolled his eyes and replied that he had "two ole women an' er gen'elman gwine ortermobublin with his cheffonier."

The conductor opined that these would prove unfertile candidates for McGinnis. He therefore turned to Moses, of car No. 2201. Moses, however, had only half a load. There was a fat man, a Mr. Huber, who traveled regularly; two ladies on passes; and a very thin man, with his wife, her sister, a maid, two nurses, and three children.

"Nothin' doin'!" remarked the captain. "Now, Colonel, what have *you* got?"

But the Colonel, a middle-aged colored man of aristocratic appearance, had an easy answer. His entire car was full, as he expressed it, "er frogs."

"Frenchmen!" grunted McGinnis.

The conductor remembered. Yes, they were Sanko's Orchestra going on to give a matinée concert in Providence.

The next car had only five drummers, every one of whom was known to the conductor as taking the trip twice a week. They were, therefore, counted out. That left only one car, No. 2205.

"Well, William, what have you got?"

William grinned. Though sleepy, he realized the importance of the disclosure he was about to make and was correspondingly dignified and ponderous. There was two trabblin' gen'elmen, Mr. Smith and Mr. Higgins. He'd handled dose gen'elmen fo' several years. There was a very old lady, her daughter and maid. Then there was Mr. Uberheimer, who got off at Middletown. And then—William smiled significantly—there was an awful strange pair in the drawin'-room. They could look for themselves. He didn't know nuff'n 'bout burglars in disguise, but dere was "one of 'em in er mighty curious set er fixtures."

"Huh! *Two* of 'em!" commented McGinnis.

"That's easy!" remarked the mollified conductor.

The telegraph operator, who read Laura Jean Libbey, now approached with his revolver.

McGinnis, another detective, and the conductor moved toward the car. William preferred the safety of the platform and the temporary distinction of being the discoverer of the fugitive. No light was visible in the drawing-room, and the sounds of heavy slumber were plainly audible. The conductor rapped loudly; there was no response. He rattled the door and turned the handle vigorously, but elicited no sign of recognition. Then McGinnis rapped with his knife on the glass of the door. He happened to hit three times. Immediately there were sounds within. Something very much like "All right, sir," and the door was opened. The conductor and McGinnis saw a fat man, in blue silk pajamas, his face flushed and his eyes heavy with sleep, who looked at them in dazed bewilderment.

"Wot do you want?" drawled the fat man, blinking at the lantern.

"Sorry to disturb you," broke in McGinnis briskly, "but is there any wan else, beside ye, to kape ye company?"

Wilkins shook his head with annoyance and made as if to close the door, but the detective thrust his foot across the threshold.

"Aisy there!" he remarked. "Conductor, just turn on that light, will ye?"

Wilkins scrambled heavily into his berth and the conductor struck a match and turned on the Pintsch light. Only one bed was occupied, and that by the fat man in the pajamas. On the sofa was an elegant alligator-skin bag, disclosing a row of massive silver-topped bottles. A tall silk hat and Inverness coat hung from a hook, and a suit of evening clothes, as well as a business suit of fustian, were neatly folded and lying on the upper berth.

At this vision of respectability both McGinnis and the conductor recoiled, glancing doubtfully at one another. Wilkins saw his advantage.

"May I hinquire," remarked he, with dignity, "wot you mean by these hactions? W'y am I thus disturbed in the middle of the night? It is houtrageous!"

"Very sorry, sir," replied the conductor. "The fact is, we thought *two* people, suspicious characters, had taken this room together, and this officer here"—pointing to McGinnis—"had orders to arrest one of them."

Wilkins swelled with indignation.

"Suspicious characters! Two people! Look 'ere, conductor, I'll 'ave you to hunderstand that I will not tolerate such a performance. I am Mr. McAllister, of the Colophon Club, New York, and I am hon my way to hattend the wedding of Mr. Frederick Cabot in Boston, to-morrow. I am to be 'is best man. Can I give you any further information?"

The conductor, who had noticed the initials "McA" on the silver bottle heads, and the same stamped upon the bag, stammered something in the nature of an apology.

"Say, Cap.," whispered McGinnis, "we've got him wrong, I guess. This feller ain't no burglar. Anywan can see he's a swell all right. Leave him alone."

"Very sorry to have disturbed you," remarked the conductor humbly, putting out the light and closing the door.

"That nigger must be 'nutty,'" he added to the detective. "By Joshua! Perhaps he's got away with some of my stuff!"

"Look here, William, what's the matter with you? Have you been swipin' my whisky? They're ain't two men in that drawin'-room at all—just one—a swell," hollered the conductor, as they reached the platform.

"Fo' de Lawd, Cap'n, I ain't teched yo' whisky," cried William in terror. "I swear dey was two of 'em, 'n' de udder was in *dis*guise. It was de fines' *dis*guise I ebber saw!" he added reminiscently.

"Aw, what yer givin' us!" exclaimed McGinnis, entirely out of patience. "What kind av a disguise was he in?"

"Dat's what I axed him," explained William, edging toward the rim of the circle. "I done ax him right away what character he done represent. He had on silk stockin's, an' a colored deglishay shirt, an' a belt an' mocassins, an' a sword an'—"

"A sword!" yelled McGinnis, making a jump in William's direction. "I'll break yer black head for ye!"

"Hold on," cried the conductor, who had disappeared into the car and had emerged again with a bottle in his hand. "The stuff's here."

"I tell ye the coon is drunk!" shouted the detective in angry tones. "He can't make small av *me*."

"I done tole you the truth," continued William from a safe distance, his teeth and eyeballs shining in the moonlight.

"Well, where did he go?" asked the conductor. "Did you put him in the drawin'-room?"

"I seen his ticket," replied William. "An' he said he wanted to smoke, so he went into the 'Benvolio,' the car behin'."

"Car behind!" cried McGinnis. "There ain't no car behind. This here is the last car."

"Sure," said the conductor, with a laugh, "we dropped the 'Benvolio' at Selma Junction for repairs. Say, McGinnis, you better have that drink."

IV

McAllister was awakened by a sense of chill. The compartment was dark, save for the pale light of the moon, hanging low over what seemed to be water and the masts of ships, which stole in and picked out sharply the silver buckles on his shoes and the buttons of his doublet. There was no motion—no sound. The train was apparently waiting somewhere, but McAllister could not hear the engine. He put on his ulster and stepped to the door of the car. All the lights had been extinguished and he could hear neither the sound of heavy breathing nor the other customary evidences of the innocent rest of the human animal. He looked across the platform for his own car and found that the train had totally disappeared. The "Benvolio" was stationary—side-tracked, evidently, on the outskirts of a town, not far from some wharfs.

"Jiminy!" thought McAllister, looking at his uncheerful surroundings and his picturesque, if somewhat cool, costume.

For a moment his mental processes refused to answer the heavy draft upon them. Then he turned up his coat-collar, stepped out upon the platform, and lit a cigar. By the light of the match he looked at his watch and saw that it was four o'clock. Overhead the sky glowed with thousands of twinkling stars, and the moon, just touching the sea, made a limpid path of light across the water. At the docks silent ships lay fast asleep. A mile away a clock struck four, intensifying the stillness. It was very beautiful, but very cold, and McAllister shivered as he thought of Wilkins, and Freddy Cabot and the wedding at twelve o'clock. So far as he knew he might be just outside of Boston—Quincy or somewhere,—yet, somehow, the moon didn't look as if it were at Quincy.

He jumped down and started along the track. His feet stung as they struck the cinder. His whole body was asleep. It was easy enough to walk in the direction in which the clock had sounded, and this he did. The rails followed the shore for about a hundred yards and then joined the main line. Presently he came in sight of a depot. Every now and then his sword would get between his legs, and this caused him so much annoyance that he took it off and carried it. It was queer how uncomfortable the old style of shoe was when used for walking on a railroad track! His ruffle, too, proved a confounded nuisance, almost preventing a satisfactory adjustment of coat-collar. Finally he untied it and put it in the pocket of his ulster. The cap was not so bad.

The depot had inspired the clubman with distinct hope, but as he approached it appeared as dark and tenantless as the car behind him. It was impossible to read the name of the station owing to the fact that the sign was too high up for the light of a match to reach it. It was clear that there was nothing to do but to wait for the dawn, and he settled himself in a corner near the express office and tried to forget his discomfort.

He had less time to wait than he had expected. Soon a great clattering of hoofs caused him to climb stiffly to his feet again. Three farmers' wagons, each drawn by a pair of heavy horses, backed in against the platform, and their drivers, throwing down the reins, leaped to the ground. All were smoking pipes and chaffing one another loudly. Then they began to unload huge cans of milk. This looked encouraging. If they were bringing milk at this hour there must be a train—going somewhere. It didn't matter where to McAllister, if only he could get warm. Presently a faint humming came along the rails, which steadily increased in volume until the approaching train could be distinctly heard.

"Pretty nigh on time," commented the nearest farmer. McAllister stepped forward, sword in hand. The farmer involuntarily drew back.

"Wall, I swan," he remarked, removing his pipe.

"Do you mind telling me," inquired our friend, "what place this is, and where this train goes to?"

"I reckon not," replied the other. "This is Selma Junction, and this here train is due in New York at five. Who be you?"

"Well," answered McAllister, "I'm just an humble citizen of New York, forced by circumstances to return to the city as soon as possible."

"Reckon you're one o' them play-actors, bean't ye?"

"You've got it," returned McAllister. "Fact is, I've just been playin' Henry VIII—on the road."

"I've heard tell on't," commented the rustic. "But I ain't never seen it. Shakespeare, ain't it?"

"Yes, Shakespeare," admitted the clubman.

At this moment the milk-train roared in and the teamsters began passing up their cans. There were no passenger coaches—nothing but freight-cars and a caboose. Toward this our friend made his way. There did not seem to be any conductor, and without making inquiries, McAllister climbed upon the platform and pushed open the door. If warmth was what he desired he soon found it. The end of the car was roughly fitted with half a dozen bunks, two chairs and some spittoons. A small cast-iron stove glowed red-hot, but while the place was odoriferous its temperature was grateful to the shivering McAllister. The car was empty save for a gigantic Irishman sitting fast asleep in the farther corner.

Our hero laid down his sword, threw off his ulster, and hung his cap upon an adjacent hook. In a moment or two the train started again. Still no one came into the caboose. Now daylight began to filter in through the grimy windows. The sun jumped suddenly from behind a ridge and shot a beam into the face of the sleeper at the other end of the car. Slowly he awoke, yawned, rubbed his eyes, and, catching the glint of silver buttons, gazed stupidly in McAllister's direction. The random glance gradually gave place to a stare of intense amazement. He wrinkled his brows and leaned forward, scrutinizing with care every detail of McAllister's make-up. The train stopped for an instant and a burly brakeman banged open the door and stepped inside. He, too, hung fire, as it were, at the sight of Henry VIII. Then he broke into a loud laugh.

"Who in thunder are *you?*"

Before McAllister could reply McGinnis, with a comprehensive smile, made answer:

"Shure, 'tis only a prisoner I'm after takin' back to the city!"

"Mr. McAllister," remarked Conville, two hours later, as the three of them sat in the visitors' room at the club, "I hope you won't say anything about this. You see, I had no business to put a kid like Ebstein on the job, but I was clean knocked out and had to snatch some sleep. I suppose he thought he was doin' a big thing when he nailed you for a burglar. But, after all, the only thing that saved Welch was your fallin' asleep in the 'Benvolio.' "

"My dear Baron," sympathetically replied McAllister, who had once more resumed his ordinary attire, "why attribute to chance what is in fact due to intellect? No, I won't mention our adventure, and if our friend McGinnis—"

"Oh, McGinnis'll keep his head shut, all right, you bet!" interrupted Barney. "But say, Mr. McAllister, on the level, you're too good for us. Why don't you chuck this game and come in out of the rain? You'll be up against it in the end. Help us to land this feller!"

McAllister took a long pull at his cigar and half closed his eyes. There was a quizzical look around his mouth that Conville had never seen there before.

"Perhaps I will," he said softly. "Perhaps I will."

"Good!" shouted the Baron; "put it there! Now, if you *get* anything, tip us off. You can always catch me at 3100 Spring."

"Well," replied the clubman, "don't forget to drop in here, if you happen to be goin' by. Sometime, on a rainy day, you might want a nip of somethin' warm."

But to this the Baron did not respond.

A plunge in the tank and a comfortable smoke almost restored McAllister's customary equanimity. Weddings were a bore, anyway. Then he called for a telegraph blank and sent the following:

"Was unavoidably delayed. Terribly disappointed. If necessary, use Wilkins. McA."

To which, about noontime, he received the following reply:

"Don't understand. Wilkins arrived, left clothes and departed. You must have mixed your dates. Wedding to-morrow. F. C."

"MR. DOOLEY ON CORPORAL PUNISHMENT"

BY F. P. DUNNE

"MR. DOOLEY ON CORPORAL PUNISHMENT"

BY F. P. DUNNE

"WELL, sir," said Mr. Dooley, "I see that some school-teachers down East have been petitioning to be allowed to slug th' young."

"How's that?" asked Mr. Hennessy.

"Well," said Mr. Dooley "they say they can't do anything with these tender little growths onless they use a club. They want the boord iv iddycation to restore what's called corporal punishment—that is th' fun iv lickin' some wan that can't fight back. Says wan iv thim: 'Th' little wans undher our care are far fr'm bein' th' small angels that they look. As a matter iv fact they are rebellyous monsthers that must be suppressed be vigorous an',' says he, 'stern measures. Is it right,' says he, 'that us schoolmasthers shud daily risk our lives at th' hands iv these feerocious an' tigerish inimies iv human s'ciety without havin' a chance to pound them? Yisterdah a goolden haired imp iv perdition placed a tack in me chair. To-day I found a dead rat in the desk. At times they write opprobyous epithets about me on th' blackboord; at other times crood but pinted carrycachures. Nawthin' will conthrol thim. They hurl the murdherous spitball. They pull th' braid iv th' little girl. They fire baseballs through th' windows. Sometimes lumps iv chewin' gum are found undher their desks where they have stuck thim f'r further use. They shuffle their feet whin I'm narvous. They look around thim when they think I'm not lookin'. They pass notes grossly insultin' each other. Moral suasion does no good. I have thried writin' to their parents askin' thim to cripple their offspring, an' th' parents have come over an' offered to fight me. I've thried keepin' thim afther school, makin' thim write compositions an' shakin' th' milk teeth out iv thim, but to no avail. Me opinyon is that th' av'rage small boy is a threecherous, dangerous crather like th' Apachy Indyan an' that th' on'y thing to do with him is to slam him with a wagon spoke,' says he.

"An th' boord iv iddycation is discussin' th' petition. It can't quite make up its mind whether Solomon wasn't right. Solomon said, accordin' to Hogan, spile th' rod an' save th' child. He must've had a large fam'ly if he was annywhere near Tiddy Rosenfelt's law iv av'rages. I don't see how he cud've spared time f'r writin' from correctin' his fam'ly. He must've set up nights. Annyhow, th' boord iv iddycation is discussin' whether he was right or not. I don't know mes'lf. All I know is that if I was a life insurance canvasser or a coal dealer or something else that made me illegible to be a mimber iv a board iv iddycation, an' an able-bodied man six feet tall come to me f'r permission to whale a boy three feet tall, I'd say: 'I don't know whether ye are compitint. Punishing people requires special thrainin'. It ain't iv'rybody that's suited f'r th' job. Ye might bungle it. Just take off ye'er coat an' vest an' step into th' next room an' be examined.' An' in th' next room th' ambitious iddycator wud find James J. Jeffreys or some other akely efficient expert ready f'r him an' if he come back alive he'd have a certy-ficate entitlin' him to whack anny little boy he met—except mine.

"Sure there'd be very few people to say they believed in corporal punishment if corporal punishment was gin'ral. I wudden't give anny wan th' right to lick a child that wanted to lick a child. No wan shud be licked till he's too old to take a licking. If it's right to larrup an infant iv eight why ain't it right to larrup wan iv eighteen? Supposin' Prisidint Hadley iv Yale see that th' left tackle or th' half back iv th' football team wasn't behavin' right. He'd been caught blowin' a pea shooter at th' pro-fissor iv iliminthry chemisthry, or pullin' th' dure bell iv th' pro-fissor iv dogmatic theosophy. He don't know any diff'rent. He's not supposed to ralize th' distinction between right an' wrong yet. Does Prisidint Hadley grab th' child be th' ear an' conduct him to a corner iv th' schoolroom an wallup him? Ye bet he does not. Prisidint Hadley may be a bold man in raisin' money or thranslatin' Homer, but he knows th' diff'rence between courage and sheer recklessness. If he thried to convince this young idea how to shoot in this careless way ye'd read in the pa-apers that th' fire department was thryin' to rescue Prisidint Hadley fr'm th' roof iv th' buildin' but he declined to come down.

"But what wud ye do with a child that refused to obey ye?" demanded Mr. Hennessy.

"Not bein' ayther a parent or an iddycator I niver had such a child," said Mr. Dooley. "I don't know what I'd do if I was. Th' on'y thing I wudden't do wud be to hit him if he cudden't hit back, an' thin I'd think twice about it. Th' older I grow th' more things there are I know I don't know annything about. An' wan iv thim is childher. I can't figure thim out at all.

"What d'ye know about thim little wans that ye have so carefully reared be lavin' thim in th' mornin' befure they got up an' losin' ye'er temper with at night whin ye come home fr'm wurruk? They don't know ye an' ye don't know thim. Ye'll niver know till 'tis too late. I've often wondhered what a little boy thinks about us that call oursilves grown up because we can't grow anny more. We wake him up in th' mornin' whin he wants to sleep. We make him wash his face whin he knows it don't need washin' thin as much as it will later an' we sind him back to comb his hair in a way he don't approve iv at all. We fire him off to school just about th' time iv day whin anny wan ought to be out iv dures. He trudges off to a brick buildin' an' a tired teacher tells him a lot iv things he hasn't anny inthrest in at all, like how manny times sivin goes into a hundhred an' nine an' who was King iv England in thirteen twinty-two an' where is Kazabazoo on the map. He has to set there most iv th' pleasant part iv th' day with sixty other kids an' ivry time he thries to do annything that seems right to him like jabbin' a frind with a pin or carvin' his name on the desk, th' sthrange lady or gintleman that acts as his keeper swoops down on him an' makes him feel like a criminal. To'rds evenin' if he's been good an' repressed all his nacharal instincts he's allowed to go home an' chop some wood. Whin he's done that an' has just managed to get a few iv his frinds together an' they're beginnin' to get up inthrest in th' spoort iv throwin' bricks down into a Chinese laundhry his little sister comes out an' tells him he's wanted at home. He instinctively pulls her hair an' goes in to study his lessons so that he'll be able to-morrow to answer some ridiklous questions that are goin' to be asked him. Afther a while ye come home an' greet him with ye'er usual glare an' ye have supper together. Ye do most iv th' talkin', which ain't much. If he thries to cut in with somethin' that inteligent people ought to talk about ye stop him with a frown. Afther supper he's allowed to study some more, an' whin he's finished just as th' night begins to look good he's fired off to bed an' th' light is taken away fr'm him an' he sees ghosts an' hobgoberlins in th' dark an' th' next he knows he's hauled out iv bed an' made to wash his face again.

"An' so it goes. If he don't do anny iv these things or if he doesn't do thim th' way ye think is th' right way some wan hits him or wants to. Talk about happy childhood. How wud ye like to have twinty or thirty people issuin' foolish ordhers to ye, makin' ye do things ye didn't want to do, an' niver undherstandin' at all why it was so? 'Tis like livin' on this earth an' bein' ruled by the inhabitants iv Mars. He has his wurruld, ye can bet on that, an' 'tis a mighty important wurruld. Who knows why a kid wud rather ate potatoes cooked nice an' black on a fire made of sthraw an' old boots thin th' delicious oatmeal so carefully an' so often prepared f'r him be his kind parents? Who knows why he thinks a dark hole undher a sidewalk is a robber's cave? Who knows why he likes to collect in wan pocket a ball iv twine, glass marbles, chewin' gum, a dead sparrow an' half a lemon? Who knows what his seasons are? They are not mine, an' they're not ye'ers, but he goes as reg'lar fr'm top time to marble time an' fr'm marble time to kite time as we go fr'm summer to autumn an' autumn to winter. To-day he's thryin' to annihilate another boy's stick top with his; to-morrow he's thrying to sail a kite out iv a tillygraft wire. Who knows why he does it?

"Faith we know nawthin' about him an' he knows nawthin' about us. I can raymimber whin I was a little boy but I can't raymimber how I was a little boy. I call back as though it was yisterdah th' things I did, but why I did thim I don't know. Faith if I cud look for'ard to th' things I've done I cud no more aisily explain why I was goin' to do thim. Maybe we're both wrong in the way we look at each other—us an' th' childher. We think we've grown up an' they don't guess that we're childher. If they knew us betther they'd not be so surprised at our actions an' wudden't foorce us to hit thim. Whin ye issued some foolish ordher to ye'er little boy he'd say: 'Pah-pah is fractious to-day. Don't ye think he ought to have some castor ile.' "

"It's a wise child that knows his own father," said Mr. Hennessy.

"It's a happy child that doesn't," said Mr. Dooley.

THE PROBATIONER AND THE PENNANT

BY HUGH PENDEXTER

THE PROBATIONER AND THE PENNANT

BY HUGH PENDEXTER

SHE met her husband at the porch door in sour anxiety and, with thin lips pursed, waited for him to speak. He surveyed her harsh face and gaunt figure with twinkling eyes for a few seconds, and then nodded his white head delightedly and, catching her about the waist with one brawny arm, lightly swung her to the window. Exultantly he pointed to three men receding down the road, one of them with flowing whiskers streaming sideways, which gave him a fluffy and one-sided appearance.

"Yas, Sarah," cried he, "it's Brother Sedgwick and several of the class members."

"Drat the man!" she exclaimed, disengaging his arm and returning to add vinegar to her steaming pickles. "I seen 'em call at the barn, didn't I? But as I've seen 'em call on you many times before, when their errand brought sorrer to my heart, I want to know what they've decided."

He straightened complacently and was preparing to give her a leisurely account of the interview, when she noisily dropped a stick of wood into the stove and fixed on him a look of impatience that was accentuated by the veil of sparks, and he hurried to add, "It's all right this time. I'm to be taken into full membership this coming Sunday."

"Thank the Lawd!" she cried, counterfeiting a sob. "Then, Emory Annit, your long probation is ended at last and you'll quit worrying me and can now have the blessed privilege of worshiping in my church."

His face drew down and he plucked at his clean-shaven chin dubiously. "Why, Sarah, I thought it had been my church all along, seeing how I've been on probation all the time—"

"For a mighty long time," she interrupted.

"Wal, my dear, it's been overlong, I'll admit," he sighed. Then, brightening, "But it shows I was set on breaking in some time. Now be fair; ain't I tried my dangdest to join the church?"

"No, Emory," she denied with artificial evenness. "You've always allowed something to crop out to hinder."

He coughed apologetically and hung his head, while the fine old face struggled between a whimsical smile and a contrite expression. "Wal, we'll waive that p'int," he said, eying her furtively. "I'll only say I've been on the ragged edge of being taken in a dozen times."

"Gambling is a sin and taking part in trivial things is onreligious," she reminded him sententiously. "Of course ye remember why ye wa'nt taken in last year."

"Not in particular," he returned, knitting his brows as if endeavoring to recollect.

"I s'pose not," she said in her best sarcastic vein. "Nor anything about winning a hoss race by waving your hat in the face of Lem Tibbetts's hoss and making him bolt when ye was at the back of the track."

He stifled a frightened grin and frowned heavily. "I was protecting myself," he protested earnestly. "We was going it neck and neck and Lem's hired man was hiding in the bushes to throw a rock at me so's I'd lose. I waved my hat like this," and he fluttered a hand lightly, pantomimic of a falling leaf, or the lazy drifting of rifle smoke, "jest to distract his attention."

"Then why did the poor brute try to climb over the fence?" she inquired skeptically. "And why did ye offer to bet Lem a dollar ye could best him again?"

"I knew he wouldn't bet, my dear," he said in mild deprecation, now seeking to retreat.

"And it all happened on a Saturday," she continued in a dry monotone, "and on the next day ye wa'n't taken into the church."

"That's so," he groaned, his mouth describing a downward curve. Then he pleaded, "But Sarah, jest because a man loves a hoss trot and a baseball game and to see the cattle pull, and is foolish enough to wager—once in a very great while—a measly five-cent seegar on a result, he ain't so awful wicked. Ye really don't believe the Lawd loves me any the less for that, do ye?"

"I was brought up to believe He frowns on such rinktums," she returned.

He met her steady, convincing gaze for some seconds as she stood with spoon poised above the kettle. Then as the spoon fell he bowed his head ruefully, and declared, "Wal, it's all over now. I'm through. As such carrying-ons is foolish and have kept me out of the church, I've quit 'em. I wouldn't bet a seegar on the best race ever pulled off—no, not if I was driving. I wouldn't go across the road to see the best ball ever pitched—that is, I don't think I would."

"And knowing your weakness, and remembering how many times you've backslid at the last minute, you'll keep away from temptation, such as the ball game to-morrer," she suggested almost pleasantly, but very firmly.

He winced slightly and drummed several tattooes on the window-pane before replying faintly, "I s'pose I'll have to. I really don't care much about going; only, I don't want to seem to doubt my moral strength. Of course there's no harm in my standing in the background and quietly looking on. A church-member who has to scuttle to cover every time a high-stepper sweeps by, or when a man steals second base, can't be of much value to the Lawd. I might as well be in a convent if I can't walk abroad like other men."

She straightened her pessimistic lips in a determined line and removed the vinegar quietly, as if fearing to disturb a sleeper. "Ye think it ain't safe for me to go?" he persisted anxiously. "Ye think I really care about going and will hoot and cut up and disgrace myself and be refused membership on the Sabbath?"

In a low discord she began humming a hymn, and proceeded to fill little bags with spice. He gazed long and vacantly on the hearth, all enthusiasm blotted from his face. Gradually, however, his eyes snapped as he happened upon some pleasing retrospect, and half fearfully he asked, "S'pose young Whitten's going to pitch for our boys to-morrer?"

A nutmeg-grater dropped with a clatter and she

turned a gaze of grim suspicion on his averted face. He scowled at the stove and, still avoiding her accusing eyes, sought refuge in the observation, "Of course I don't care; only, I was thinking, in a dreamy sort of a way, that with the Whitten boy pitching, we—er, Peevy's Mills oughter win."

Still no comment from her, rigid and distrustful. "Not that I care much about it, as my thoughts are elsewhere," he confidentially explained to the stove.

"Your thoughts," she suggested bitterly, "are probably on the time ye was put on further probation for threatening to lick the empire."

"Never intended to harm a hair of his head," he began earnestly. "He robbed—"

"Wal, ye won't be robbed this time," she broke in, now confronting him in ultimate assurance. "To-morrer ye keep away from that game and be ready Sunday with a clear conscience and a new shirt to go with me to church. We don't want no church-members who act like circuses. To-morrer ye can fuss with the garden fence."

And the morrow found him fetching his tools from the barn; but despite the glory of the day and the anticipation of the Sabbath's reward, there was the shadow of a cloud upon his face. Temptation whispered that he could view the game in placid, dignified quiet; but his honest old heart warned him that he would be in the thickest of any argument, yelling himself hoarse and disporting his sixty-odd years in a manner sure to arouse the class-leader's condemnation. So he bowed to his fate and a broken gate by the roadside.

"Oh, Mr. Annit"—a youthful voice caused him to look

up—"Jim Whitten's arm is gone lame and we ain't no one to take his place this afternoon."

Emory dropped his hammer and raised himself on his knees with sympathetic dismay creasing his face. "Arm gone back on him, Wilbur?" he cried.

The youth, seeing in the old man only another of his kind, approached nearer. "It has," he almost sniveled; "but we mustn't let on, Mr. Annit."

"Sh-h-h, not a word," agreed Emory, tapping his nose knowingly. "Who pitches for the others?"

"Watkins."

"Huh!" groaned Emory, his mouth sinking another notch. "Wal, I'm glad I'm not going to see it."

"Mr. Annit!" gasped the boy, dropping in despair on the bank. "Not going to see it?"

"No, Wilbur," replied Emory gently, resuming his work and whistling mechanically. "No, Wilbur, I have more serious things to think of."

"Not going to be there?" choked the boy, tearing up the grass.

Emory felt a sharp twinge of pain as he stole a glance at the half-crying face, and in a tremulous voice he said soothingly: "Of course my sympathies will be with ye, and I shall hope, as I think of it whenever I hear the cheering, that our boys win."

"The game is lost already," said Wilbur bitterly, rising. "I never could have believed, Mr. Annit, that you'd ever forsake us. But there, we've got a losing team, which makes some difference."

"Wilbur!" cried Emory, staggering to his feet and shaking a finger before the upturned freckled face, "if ye ever say anything like that again I'll larrup ye, jest to prove I still have ye and them other younkers in mind. Why, what d'ye mean, ye ungrateful young— Forsake the boys! Why, God bless my soul! when did I ever forsake 'em?"

"Never till now," whimpered Wilbur.

"Wal, I ain't doing it now," defended Emory weakly. "I'm preparing for weighty things and a more serious life. I'm gitting too old to be chasing after such rinktums." Then, with pride: "Ye see, I'm to be taken into the church to-morrer, and I can't go there fresh from howling myself hoarse and sassing the empire at a ball game. I'm composing my mind to-day, for to-morrer will be a proud day for me." And the hint of a tear glistened in his boyish blue eyes. "And, Wilbur, I want ye to tell the others I ain't forgot 'em, and that this strong right arm," and he bunched corded muscles that time had only increased, "and this old voice is always at their sarvice when it don't interfere with Christian grace and dignity. And, Wilbur, tell 'em all to be at church to-morrer to enjoy my victory over the flesh, as well as to stay to Sunday-school. I'll be there to teach the class, ye know."

"I'll tell 'em and I'll be there for one," sighed the boy, his face softening.

"That's right," cried the old man heartily. "It's a bully lesson, Wilbur. All about the Saviour and the children. He never forgot the younkers."

"I guess that's so," muttered the boy, half abashed.

"No, sirree!" continued Emory joyously. "And I guess I love Him best when he had the children around Him. He never sent 'em away, ye see, and He never kept away from 'em, either."

"I know," mumbled the boy bashfully.

Emory stroked his chin in silence for a few seconds and looked up into the blue. "Never kept away from 'em," he repeated only half aloud. Then abruptly, "What time does the game begin?"

"Two o'clock," was the listless response.

"Umph. Never quit 'em when He could be with 'em, in their study or in their play, did He? No, sirree! Of course not. Two o'clock, eh? All right, Wilbur. Have a brave heart and tell Jim Whitten to daub on a little more liniment. Good-by."

The rough pasture lot was fringed with spectators as the two nines opened the last game of the season. The year before, the visitors had won the series. Now the teams were tied and with young Whitten in poor form, it looked as if a second defeat would be scored for Peevy's Mills. The men lounged quietly about on knolls and rocks and whittled thoughtfully. The women frowned at the deft practise of the visitors and openly exchanged expressions of condolence, careless that supporters of the visitors might overhear.

Now it was a curious thing that though Mrs. Annit had prohibited her husband from attending the game, she herself had yielded to the pleadings of Mr. Sedgwick's wife and had joined the outer ring of bystanders. She had not deemed it necessary to inform her spouse of her destination when she left the house, and was now calm and complacent in the knowledge that she was ever immune from unseemly enthusiasm. It was also comforting to realize that though she had denied him the spectacle, she could make it possible for him to enjoy an eye-witness's report of the game. Only, he must not be thus delectated until safely within the church.

At the outset, young Whitten pitched with all his old-time vigor, but the knowing ones detected a disposition to hurry through the game, as if he had just so much energy to be used within a given period of time. For two innings not a man on either side passed first base, and Peevy's Mills began to wax confident and to discredit all rumors of a lame arm. But in the third one of the visitors made a two-base hit and was advanced to third on a single, with none out.

"I can't see how folks with mature minds can enjoy a thing like this," Mrs. Annit was yawning as the spectators gloomily awaited the first score, apparently inevitable, when a deep voice boomed across the pasture, "Remember the play, Wilbur."

Mrs. Annit, with an ejaculation of angry surprise, craned her neck to scan the outskirts of the crowd across the diamond. "D'ye hear that voice?" she muttered grimly to her companion. "D'ye hear that pesky man of mine? And him expecting to be admitted to-morrer."

But Mrs. Sedgwick, with mouth agape and with eyes only for the sport, was eagerly noting the swift change now apparent in the home team's demeanor, and heard nothing. Every man had stiffened at the first word and the infield was grinning with new courage. Young Whitten almost made a balk as he followed the crowd's example and swiftly turned his head. His arm was completing a final circle as the real significance of the shouted words filtered home, and Wilbur, behind the bat, gave a sharp yelp of ecstasy and changed his signal.

And the arm, entering upon another circle, made a pretense of cutting the plate, but in reality threw wide and swift, and the man on first, confident in a goodly lead and the man on third as a deterrent, scuttled for second.

But Wilbur, heeding the old man's call, shot the ball not to second, but to the short-stop; and the man on third, deceived by the short throw, started to score. Before the spectators could remember to cheer, the ball was returned home and smacked on Wilbur's mitt —the runner was out. The next two batters went down quickly.

The shouting of the happy crowd at first drowned Mrs. Annit's remarks, but when the clamor had subsided she repeated, "I see him now. And I left him at home, reading his Bible." And in sour derision she pointed at her husband's sturdy form, now approaching the side lines.

She could hear him, too, as throwing aside all caution he wedged his way to the front ranks and assumed control of the home team. So could all the others hear him. Some said his voice carried a mile that day. Anyway, not a word was lost to the joyous players, as his shrewd old mind engineered a triumph out of difficult and dangerous situations for several innings.

Then it became obvious that young Whitten was failing fast. Instead of snapping the ball in hurriedly he paused after each delivery, as if collecting his strength, and in the eighth inning it was only the loud-voiced advice of Emory that kept the score down to five to four in favor of the enemy.

"I can't pitch another ball," sobbed the exhausted

youth, throwing himself on his face as the home team was about to take the field for the last inning.

"Jest once more," coaxed Wilbur.

"I'd do it if it killed me, if I could. But I can't," choked the boy.

"Hurry along with another pitcher," advised the umpire.

"We ain't got another one," bitterly admitted Wilbur, his face grimacing as he fought back tears of chagrin. "This is a small village and poor Jim was our only man. That's what's done him. He's pitched his arm off."

"We've got this game," cried Emory, kneeling beside the disconsolate youth, "if we can only make a shift. There must be some one."

"There ain't no one," said Wilbur in despair. "Even if we could play with eight men, there isn't a man on the team who would amount to shucks—not against these fellers."

"Can't stay here all day. If you don't want to play it out, we'll take the game," drawled the captain of the visitors. "If I had a extra man, I'd lend him to you. Either put in another pitcher—we don't care who—or else quit."

"Play ball, or lose the game," agreed the umpire. "I'll give you two minutes."

"We must git some one," whispered Emory in a shaky voice.

"Talking is all right, but who?" said Wilbur, jeering, for very bitterness of spirit. "Who is there in all Peevy's Mills that can throw even a swift, straight ball? This is the dodrottedst, dangdest—"

"Here! Quit that, young man," ordered Emory

sternly. "I played ball before your father was old enough to play marbles. So there's one. Only we threw nothing but those straight, underhand balls. I don't know anything about these curves you're all learning nowadays."

"Play ball!" cried the umpire, snapping his watch cover. And Mrs. Annit gave one low cry of horror as she beheld her husband pulling off his coat as he walked awkwardly toward the box.

"And he was going to be took in to-morrer," exclaimed Mrs. Sedgwick, while her husband, who had joined them, removed his spectacles and examined the lenses before he believed that his eyes were reporting truly. Then he grew red of face and ejaculated, "Huh!"

The monosyllable pierced Mrs. Annit like a knife and she bowed her head in shame as the grinning umpire generously offered, "I'll give you a few seconds to limber up in."

The old man winced a trifle as his eyes found the glooming face of his class-leader, but the work before him must now be done, and swinging and doubling his arm a few times he cautiously tossed a rainbow that Wilbur in complete dejection caught with one hand. "Try them a little harder," begged the boy.

"Can ye hold me?" beamed the old man, now evidencing a degree of elasticity with his right leg that caused his wife to gasp in astonishment as she peeped through her fingers.

"I could hold a cannon-ball if there was only some one to shoot it," lamented the catcher.

Emory clumsily pivoted on one heel, stabbed his toe forward, and delivered one that cut the edge of the plate and sharply snapped Wilbur's feet and head forward. "That's better," stuttered the youth; "those are the kind!"

"Batter up!" cried the umpire, and young Watkins, shaking with laughter, selected a stick and carelessly took his position.

Then did the old man's eyes bulge and before the bat could be lifted the ball slapped in Wilbur's mitt and the umpire in a hushed voice was saying, "Strike one!"

Young Watkins braced himself and gazed with new interest on the pitcher. The next ball went high and was ignored. Then, smack! it was shot back almost as soon as it touched the old man's pawing, calloused palms, and the striker realized that he had swung a second too late.

"Wal, I never!" grunted Mr. Sedgwick, adjusting his glasses more firmly and frowning heavily as he advanced a few paces.

"Oh, the burning disgrace of it!" moaned Mrs. Annit, as the jeers and cheers swept over her.

"Look!" shrieked Mrs. Sedgwick, brushing her husband aside. "He's got two strikes on the young varmint. And, mercy! ain't he going to send in a hot one now!"

"Bet ye a good five-cent seegar ye don't strike him out, Emory," challenged some one.

"Take ye!" cried the old man excitedly, working both arms in a bewildering manner as he crouched over the ball, and then spinning about like a gigantic tee-totum as he held it on high.

"What!" gasped Brother Sedgwick, dragging yet a step nearer.

"That settles all," said Mrs. Annit dully.

"Mister Smarty loses his seegar," jeered Mrs. Sedgwick, dancing wildly. For Emory, after apparently collecting every atom of strength in his tall frame, compressed it into his strong right arm, and, with a final spasmodic show of fierceness, delivered the ball, but released it so easily and slowly that young Watkins swung viciously when it was three feet from the plate.

"Abigail!" ejaculated the horrified class-leader.

"Nothing matters now," said Mrs. Annit, sadly, but with quickening eye as the crowd hoarsely applauded her husband's prowess.

"He struck him out," repeated Mrs. Sedgwick joyously, as one imparting an exclusive news item.

It was several seconds before Wilbur could control himself sufficiently to attend to his duties, and even as the ball was being delivered he stretched forth his arms in an ecstatic desire to embrace the perspiring old man. But the first ball to the next batter was only moderately swift and was promptly knocked to short with the runner retiring at first.

"Well pitched!" cheered Mrs. Sedgwick as the next man dodged.

"I'm surprised at ye," grieved her husband, pushing a small boy aside. Then decisively, "He ain't gitting 'em high enough."

As he spoke, a two-bagger was pounded out, and he sniffed heavily and frowned on the staring Mrs. Annit. "Sister, I'm sorry," he began in his official voice, when a shout caused him to wheel just in time to see a long fly captured in center field. And no scores.

"I know," she whimpered; "he's lost his chance. He's lost his chance. And him a old man."

"It's too bad," condoled Mrs. Sedgwick piously, relaxing in rigidity as the teams crossed on the diamond. "Of course the church must frown on such actions, especially in the old—"

"And especially gambling," reminded her husband gloomily, as he scanned the preliminary maneuvers of young Watkins.

"He's lost his last chance," sobbed Mrs. Annit.

"Mebbe," sighed Mrs. Sedgwick, nodding her head. Then starting forward, "But I really believe he's going to win the game."

For now that Peevy's Mills was at bat, Emory, oblivious to all but the task before him, was limping painfully along the base-line, coaching and kicking up dust as if it had been his daily work from childhood, while young Watkins scowled in nervous uncertainty. But the first man up hit short and was beaten by the ball to first.

"Don't try to strike 'em so hard. Take it easy," begged Emory of the next youth.

This advice resulted in a leisurely effort and the ball just cleared the short-stop's head.

"Oh, what has he sacrificed!" moaned Mrs. Annit, wiping her eyes and leaning forward.

"He shouldn't sacrifice," snarled the class-leader. "He should bang— But, anyhow, that's one man on base."

A pop-fly retired the next batter and sent the spectators back from the pasture into the shadows of the fringing trees.

"Pretty didoes for a would-be church-member to be cutting up," growled a townsman standing near.

"It's all over. We might as well go home," said

Mr. Sedgwick testily, clutching his wife's arm. Then to the sad-faced Mrs. Annit, "Try and bear up, sister. I'm sorry my duty called me here to witness his lack of grace, of—ah—moral fiber. Ahem. But some one must act the spy—ah—in order that gossip shall not —ahem—wrong a man. Now that we know of our own knowledge—"

"Hooray for Emory!" broke in the frenzied crowd, and in the middle of a word Sedgwick stopped and stared as one fascinated at the old man approaching the plate.

"It'll soon be over. It is over—" began Mr. Sedgwick, wetting his dry lips and unconsciously crowding forward to the base-line, closely attended by his wife and Mrs. Annit.

"Naturally a good man, too," he continued in his wife's ear, and then added, "But the sun's in his eyes and he's a goner."

Mrs. Annit, catching only the last word, changed in demeanor and countenance most wonderfully. With flashing eyes she confronted the astounded class-leader and shouted, "Ye think so, do ye? Ye think so, eh? Wal, let me tell ye, church or no church, my man ain't lost yet—"

"Why, he may make first," spluttered Sedgwick.

"Go it, Emory!" encouraged Mrs. Annit shrilly, now ignoring the Sedgwicks. "Go it! Whang that contraption out of sight."

He caught her words even above the uproar and in pleased wonder glanced up the third base-line where three figures, apart from the others, were prancing stiffly and madly waving handkerchiefs.

With a broad smile of renewed confidence he turned

to his work, but the second of inattention cost him dear, as already the umpire was reluctantly calling a strike.

"Robber!" cried a voice, which some said resembled Sedgwick's.

"Keep watch of it, Emory," shrieked a woman.

"Hooray! hooray!" clamored the crowd.

And Emory, catching the fever, stepped up and down as if treading on live coals, and pounded the plate hungrily.

"One ball!" cried the umpire.

"Wait for a nice one, husband."

"Two strikes!" continued the umpire.

"Hit it! Swat it, brother!"

"Two balls!" barked the umpire.

"Hooray! hooray!"

And Emory, setting his jaws, allowed no more to pass him, but met the next with a mighty crash, and the man on first began cantering home.

"One will tie! two will win!" sobbed Mrs. Sedgwick, and the crowd, realizing that a home run meant victory for Peevy's Mills, ran imploringly along the base-line and pleaded for the slow-footed runner to accelerate his gait.

"Oh, faster, faster, Emory!" cried the wife, as she stood wringing her hands at third and in agony watched him slowly turn second base, while the center-fielder was speeding swiftly after the ball.

"Faster. Jest a mite faster, Em," she sobbed, as with a strained, exultant face he staggered toward her, while his class-leader, with body rocking, extended his arms and gave an excellent pantomime of a man rescuing a fellow creature by pulling in a rope.

"He's got the ball!" bawled the crowd in warning as Emory turned the last corner and pounded heavily along for home.

"Slide!" bellowed the class-leader, as the fielder shot the ball to second, whence it was hurtled home. A cloud of dust answered the warning.

"He never teched him," choked Mrs. Annit, who had tottered along beside her spouse until he plunged headlong for the plate.

"Not by a foot," agreed the red-faced umpire.

"Wife, come home," commanded Mr. Sedgwick sourly as he straightened her bonnet.

An hour later Mrs. Annit stood by the kitchen sink anxiously studying her husband's bowed and dusty form.

"Emory," she said softly, "it was a nice game and ye played beautifully."

"Thanks," he returned dully.

"But I want ye to promise ye'll never play it again."

"I've quit," he sighed, not lifting his head. "Quit when it's too late."

"And—and, I want to say," she faltered, "I rather liked the dashing way ye played."

"I used to be a hummer," he confided in sad complacency.

"And—but Lawd! Here's Brother Sedgwick and some o' the other brethren."

"I'll meet 'em in the yard," he announced ruefully, as he rose.

"No," she begged, her face softened. "I'm to blame, too; I cheered ye on a bit. Let's meet it together—here."

He turned to her in wonder and rubbed his head

dubiously. "I thought ye'd have it in for me—Come in."

Brother Sedgwick headed the delegation and without accepting a chair said, after coughing dryly, "I am here on a sad errand, Brother Annit. Ye was at a ball game to-day."

The accused bowed his head meekly.

"And we also heard ye *played* in a ball game to-day and displayed a lack of dignity that ain't becoming to a church member," Brother Durgin harshly took up the charge.

"He won the game," wailed Mrs. Annit, taking her husband's hand.

"And we hear ye wagered a seegar," completed Brother Weevy sternly.

Emory sighed deeply and made an affirmative noise.

"All of which is very bad," said Brother Sedgwick sorrowfully. "The game might be overlooked, but the seegar is bad, very bad."

"He said a good five-cent—" began Emory, who had been lost in introspection.

"It's all very bad," repeated Brother Sedgwick, with a slight touch of temper.

"I know what ye mean," groaned Emory. "But it's the hardest on my wife, here. My intentions was good—"

"Ahem!" broke in the class-leader, studying the floor thoughtfully. "The ball playing could be overlooked, if ye'd promise never to play it again, or football, without the church's consent. But of course—I'm sorry to say it—the gambling—"

"I suppose it would help some if he refused to take the seegar," suggested Durgin softly.

"Refuse to take it!" cried Emory. "Why, I bet with Bill Hussey an' he'll never pay it. Wild horses couldn't drag it from him. I know, because once—"

"Tut, tut," broke in Brother Sedgwick.

"Why, then," declared Brother Weevy, "there really wa'n't no wager made. I believe, Brother Sedgwick, we—eh?"

"Why, I'm inclined to say—ahem! Mr. Annit, are ye using any liniment on that arm?" inquired the class-leader anxiously.

"No," sighed Emory.

"Wal, ye'd better. Anyhow, if it's lame to-morrer, don't let that keep ye from church."

"I'm—I'm—ye don't mean—" stuttered the old man wistfully.

"He's to be took in?" gasped Mrs. Annit.

"Yaas," drawled Brother Sedgwick, grinning lamely. "All the boys will be there. Good day." And the delegation departed.

But before the astounded couple could find words, the door creaked open a few inches and Brother Sedgwick's face, radiant with admiration, was thrust in to observe, "Great game, Em. Simply g-r-e-a-t."

BREEZY

BY J. GEORGE FREDERICK

BREEZY

BY J. GEORGE FREDERICK

WHEN the prosperous though unprogressive firm of Casper W. Leslie & Co., grocers, hired him they thought they had secured an ordinary clerk, and gave themselves no further concern. They already had a force of about a dozen clerks, besides half a dozen delivery teams. They had hired clerks for twenty years, and it was to them a troublesome and vexatious proceeding. They frowned at first at his slight frame, but when he put a prostrate sugar barrel on end with easy unconcern, all objections were immediately withdrawn.

His surname was the leveling one of Smith, and his Christian name—highly Christian—Hezekiah. His mother called him "Zeke" and his companions "Breezy."

Breezy entered upon his work whistling in supreme content. He was at the bottom of the commercial hill, and was preparing to run up to the top. He had no star-high ambitions to make him dream, no love affairs to make him forgetful, and no vices to keep him from doing his best. There wasn't a lazy tendon in his body. He was not tall. If he had been, he would have been lazy. He was short, thin, black-eyed, nervous, and muscular. Before his ponderous companions got an idea through their head, Breezy was half-way done with the action. A few thought he was a genius; but they were mistaken. Breezy was innocent of the smallest spark. He just had a heavy capital of nervous energy that made him work while others were content to lounge.

They put him behind the fruit counter. His first act was to clean it up and "fix things" generally. "Such a rum way of doing business," he muttered, quite like an experienced grocer, scowling at the hidden waste and slipshod displays of his predecessor. When he was through with the counter there was absolutely no fault to find with it. But he was not satisfied. He went into the cellar and started to saw and nail some boxes to make receptacles for various things back of his counter.

"What are you doing here?" said the pompous and obese superintendent, finding him at work.

"Oh," said Breezy carelessly, I'm just getting some boxes in shape to put dirt and tools in at my counter."

"We have got a carpenter to do that," said the superintendent, with displeasure; "get up where you belong and 'tend to your customers."

Breezy went up, and finished the boxes later while the superintendent was absent. He cleaned the fruit on his stand four times a day. "It gets so blamed mussed up," he said briskly to a fellow clerk who looked askance at the action.

"The other clerk didn't," replied his companion suggestively.

"Didn't he?" said Breezy coolly.

Of course the clerks laughed at him. His tie was

awry and of objectionable hue, and his trousers lacked the proper cut and crease.

The fruit trade was slow, and Breezy was highly impatient. The superintendent compelled him to stay behind his counter, and he had to gaze impatiently over the bustling crowd of the store, which seemed to stop at every other counter but his. Twice, when the superintendent was not about, he made a personal canvass among the shoppers and secured a number of sales. The third time he was discovered and peremptorily ordered back.

After closing time, Breezy was absent-minded and restless. The noise of the overhead cash system; the aroma of freshly roasted coffee, of bacon, and of cheese; the click of the weighing scales; the scraping of the busy scoops; the shrill staccato of the register bells and opening drawers; the rustle of the wrapping-paper; the shuffle of hurrying feet; the rumble of the drays on the cobbles outside; the incessant hum of voices, and the ever-changing panorama of shoppers—all these had become to Breezy the breath of life, and he sighed for them longingly ere the evenings were over. He had a printing press, and he set type as a means of diversion—all matter concerning the grocery store.

He set up a card and embodied in it an idea that he had conceived. He printed 500 of them—all the cardboard he had. They were invitations to the public to have any and all sorts of fruit delivered at their homes at any time by telephone orders. He laid one on Mr. Leslie's desk the next morning.

"Thompson," Breezy heard Leslie call shortly afterward to the superintendent, "this is a good idea. How many did you have printed?"

Thompson grew red. "I didn't have any printed," he replied in surprise. Leslie frowned, and called his partner, who also professed ignorance. Breezy watched them from behind the register, and then ventured forward.

"I printed them on my own press. Here are 500 more."

Leslie looked again at the card, and then raised his eyebrows at Thompson, who nodded in return, seemingly signifying that this was the clerk mentioned in some previous conversation.

"You may hand in your bill for them to the bookkeeper," said Leslie evenly; "and, Thompson, you may have them properly distributed."

He was paid for his cards, and there was also an extra dollar in his weekly pay envelope that Saturday. He promptly bought the best seat in the theater.

They found him the next week in the telephone booth, calling up successively from a list of over 100 residences. "Is this Mrs. Jones?" he would ask. "Pardon me, Mrs. Jones; this is Leslie's. We would like to sell you some groceries." And then he would enter into a conversation for an order. The other people on the line were indignant, and the exchange told him that he was not the only lung on the line. But in less than an hour Breezy had hurry orders aggregating twenty dollars, and Leslie himself closed Thompson's mouth of wrath at neglected customers by a word of commendation.

The firm's telephone trade had never been worked up, and Breezy printed announcements inviting customers to use the 'phone to send their orders. A 'phone was placed behind the fruit counter, and Breezy took the orders. He did more. "You're going to bake, aren't you?" he asked of the housewives when they ordered flour, lard, etc. "Isn't your baking-powder all gone? Don't you need some new pans? We've got a splendid new pan here. Patented. Only eight cents, too." And so on.

"Here, Mr. Thompson," he called to the superintendent as he passed one day; "who makes these sign cards?"

"Tommy, the shipping clerk," replied Thompson shortly.

"I have just thought," said Breezy reflectively, "that I might make a nicer one for this counter. May I try one?"

"Yes; but don't neglect your counter."

Breezy had just received a large quantity of splendid figs that morning, which were selling at a really attractive price. But the firm had not even given him price cards to put on them, and had not mentioned them in the newspaper ads. "How in blazes do they expect to sell these?" he grumbled. "Nobody knows anything about them."

When, therefore, he had surprised the busy shipping clerk by asking for the card-marking tools, and had made a few simple price cards for other goods, it occurred to him that he might as well make a fig sign. It was prettily lettered, and it read: "These figs are good, clean figs, and you won't be able to buy them very many days." The clerks leered at him when he put it over his figs, rearranging the boxes artistically on the counter. Thompson didn't happen around any more that day, but in the evening Breezy sought him out. The figs were all gone.

"H'm," said the superintendent, "you must have had an extra run on figs to-day."

Over the new supply that he received the next morning, the clerks read from another card: "More good, clean figs at this price. They'll only last through the day, though." It seemed as if everybody that came into the store that day bought figs. Thompson came to the fruit counter out of curiosity, attracted by the crowd there, which Breezy was waiting upon with a satisfied and dexterous alacrity. He elevated his eyebrows at the sign.

"Who made that sign?" he asked, when the crowd cleared off.

"Me," said Breezy, in a bustle at the cash register.

"H'm, h'm," said the superintendent, strolling off.

The next day it was raisins at a bargain, and Breezy's sign said: "We bought fifty boxes of these seedless raisins, and we are going to sell them at —— cents a pound until they are all gone."

"How many boxes of those seedless raisins went out to-day?" asked Thompson that evening, looking sourly at the sign. "I'm afraid they won't go very well."

"Twenty-five," answered Breezy. "What!" said Thompson, staring over his spectacles.

"Twenty-five," repeated Breezy.

"H'm, *h'm,*" said the superintendent, walking rapidly off.

The other twenty-five went the next day.

"Could have sold more," said Breezy.

"H'm," said Thompson slowly; and after a minute: "Those signs are neatly lettered."

Breezy was vigorously cleaning up.

"You may take off the dull hours," continued Thompson cautiously, "and make the signs for the whole store. We'll get an assistant at your counter." Breezy was kicking some boxes under his counter.

"D'ye hear?" said Thompson.

"Yes, sir," said Breezy.

For the next six weeks the customers at Leslie's enjoyed daily treats from the signs. There were no less than fifty to be made on busy days. The language was simple; it told the truth about the goods, and it never disappointed, and quite often there was a bit of humor in it. The obese superintendent frowned at Breezy's efforts and looked as if he half regretted his venture.

"The old guy," mused Breezy one day, as he saw Thompson deliberately tear one of them up. It was an egg sign, and read: "If you wait until to-morrow to buy these eggs at fifteen cents the dozen, they may not be as good as they are to-day!" Promptly Breezy had another one up which read: "It's throwing these eggs at you to sell them for fifteen cents the dozen. They're not bad, though."

Thompson stood before it for full two minutes before he decided to let it pass, and then walked away, murmuring, "H'm h'm."

But Breezy ran to extremes, and one day, when Leslie paused before a cheese sign and read, "Hold your nose here. It only takes the clerk two minutes by the clock to wrap up half a pound at thirty cents," he decided that he would draw the limit, and he told Breezy to take it down, which Breezy did with a rather crestfallen air. He had been particularly proud of this effort, and had stood behind his register a dozen different times during the day, to watch customers stare and break out into laughter. A week later they made him take another one down, and Mr. Leslie called him aside.

"Don't try to be so funny on your cards," he frowned. "You make nice cards when you stick to fact, but when you get humorous you are as loud as a barrel of mackerel."

Breezy grunted ungracious acquiescence, while the corners of the grocer's mouth twitched at the recollection of some of the cards. But they continued to be as flagrant as ever. Thompson complained to Leslie about it, and the proprietor sat for a few moments in deep thought.

"That boy's got too much vitality," he said, "and we'll have to give him another outlet for it. Making cards and answering the telephone isn't enough for him to do. I believe that I will put Morris at the telephone, and let Smith do our important outside business down town." The change was accordingly made, and Breezy became a sort of confidential clerk, doing most of the firm's business with the banks and the down-town offices. Characteristically, he allowed no opportunity to escape to learn the firm's manner of doing business, and its needs. He was not chary with suggestions either, and was told by the firm more than once that his advice had not been asked, and that it was therefore not very valuable. This logic Breezy utterly failed to comprehend.

His old friends smiled as he dashed by them daily on his bicycle, his hat crushed into his head and his face almost on the handle-bars.

The firm sent him to the newspaper offices to take advertising copy. The advertisements which he carried he criticized freely on the road down town. Most of his criticisms were of a decidedly adverse nature, and his opinion of the man who wrote them, the head of the firm, grew more and more contemptuous. He had learned some lessons in advertising by his card making.

One morning they sent him to a down-town firm of producers with an order for twenty tubs of butter. With the order they gave him copy to take to all the morning papers, making commonplace and altogether unattractive mention—thought Breezy—of a proposed special sale of these twenty tubs of butter.

"That's the weakest thing yet," he soliloquized, as he sped down the empty avenue. "Butter'll go up three cents a pound one of these days."

As he stood in the office of the company, he heard a man say something confidentially to the produce man and a customer that made him wink hard. It was that butter would go up in a few days. The customer did not seem to take it very seriously, but Breezy construed it into a mighty tip.

"Just what I thought," he said to himself. "That slow firm buying only twenty tubs!" It occurred to him that he might telephone to the firm and give them the tip; but he immediately rejected the idea.

"They'd only laugh and tell me that I wasn't running their business."

Then was born a great idea. An instant later he was decided. The producer whistled when Breezy handed him an order for a hundred tubs.

"It'll take all we have," he said.

Breezy sat down at a desk and wrote something rapidly. The foreman at the newspaper composing rooms looked at him in surprise as he gave directions about border and type, technicalities which he had learned as editor of the school paper.

The tubs were all delivered in the afternoon. Thompson came out in the wareroom and looked at the first batch of twenty. "*I* wouldn't have ordered twenty!" he said, shaking his head. "I told Jim they wouldn't go." He wasn't in when the rest came. "Are they turning the store into a butter house?" said the shipping clerk, grumbling, as he helped the men bring them in.

"Great heavens!" ejaculated Thompson the next morning when he came into the wareroom. "Where does all this butter come from?"

The shipping clerk looked unintelligent, and made no answer. Thompson brought in the head of the firm, Mr. Leslie. He, in turn, stared dumbly at the tiers of tubs.

"What the—!" he began excitedly. "I told you to order twenty, didn't I?"

"You advised me not to buy *more,*" said Thompson stiffly, "and I didn't."

"Can't you count?" exclaimed Leslie wrathfully, pointing to the tubs. "There's a hundred there, if there's one!"

When Breezy was finally called in, he faced both men easily.

"How many tubs of butter did you order?" asked Leslie.

"One hundred."

"I told you twenty!" roared Thompson.

Leslie did not answer, but made for the telephone. The produce people firmly refused to take back the tubs. "We've just refilled our refrigerators, and can't accommodate any more," they said. But they added something more in a telephone whisper. "Mr. Leslie," said Breezy, when the proprietor rang off, without any visible allayment of his wrath, "I was ordered to get only twenty, but I made it a hundred, and—"

"You did, did you?" burst out Leslie, glaring at Breezy with unutterable derision. "You'll be advertising yourself as proprietor of this store shortly, won't you?"

"But, Mr. Leslie," protested Breezy, "butter's going up in a few days!"

"Great guns!" roared Leslie, "are—are you running this firm, you—you impudent young fool? You young barrel of gall! I've a notion to break your—head!"

Breezy flushed angrily.

"Go out and draw your salary, and never set foot here again!"

Breezy turned on his heel and walked out, without looking at the clerks who had assembled at the wareroom door, attracted by the loud voices.

"Fools! fools!" he muttered between his teeth, as he drove his bicycle along the street.

When he looked at copies of all the morning papers. in which appeared the advertisements he had prepared the day before, in lieu of the originals, he smiled in genuine artistic gratification.

"If that don't sell butter," he chuckled, "nothing ever will." The advertisement predicted that butter would go up very soon, and that Leslie & Co. had bought, in anticipation of this, 100 tubs, which they would sell at one cent below the market price.

"There will be a still awfuller row in that shanty when they see these. They might arrest me." But the spirit of Breezy rose hopefully to the possibility. "If they only wait till to-night."

He learnt afterward that the store was crowded with butter buyers from early morning until late in the afternoon, and that his advertisements had precipitated the coming rise in price, and an advance of one cent was already asked that same day.

It was during the afternoon of the next day that Breezy received a note asking him to call at the office of the grocery firm of Leslie & Co.

"See here, young man," said Leslie to him in his private office, "what you did on Tuesday was a thing that could have put you behind prison bars. Do you understand?"

Privately, Breezy was skeptical, but he nodded doggedly, thinking that Leslie merely wished to abuse him, and regretting that he had come at all.

"It was pure malicious mischief in the eyes of the law," continued Leslie, "and an entirely unpardonable offense. But while this is undoubtedly so"—he talked more moderately and less harshly—"it—well, to be frank, those ads—" The remembrance of this part of Breezy's misdemeanor swelled his indignation, and he was again angry. "Those ads," he continued, "that you dutched for us—well, it was worth six months at hard confinement itself!" He glared impotently, while he got red in the face.

"Well," he began again, "as I was saying, those ads—er—well, they drew the trade, in brief, and we sold the whole hundred tubs!"

He said this as though it was little short of miracculous. Breezy did not wink an eye. To him it was the natural result.

As Breezy still held his peace, Leslie resumed: "As a result we are—er—have cleared, well, some hundred dollars."

Breezy still remained silent, and Leslie put on a pompous frown.

"Understand, young man," he declaimed, "in giving you the position of superintendent and advertising manager of this store, we most certainly wish to express our vehement displeasure at your act of Tuesday, lucky as it happened to turn out, and solemnly warn you that a repetition of such a monstrous offense will mean instant discharge. To hold this position, you will have to confine yourself to reasonable and cautious methods of doing business. Your salary will be three times your former one. Get out now, and don't bother me, but show up ready for work Monday morning."

The only evidence Breezy gave of his satisfaction with this interview was that he rode madly up the full length of the steepest hill in the city on his way home, to rid himself of surplus nervous energy.

THE FOREHANDED COLQUHOUNS

BY MARGARET WILSON

THE FOREHANDED COLQUHOUNS

BY MARGARET WILSON

"PERHAPS I'm too old to be wearing such things, but I love bright colors, and there's not a bit of use denying it."

Mary Ann gathered one end of the fancy tartan into a handful, and looked approvingly at its soft, heavy folds.

"Particularly at this time of year. It's warming to the blood on a cold autumn day just to see a dress like this on the street. I always did like a good rich tartan. It becomes me, too. Look, Selina'n'Jane."

She held the dress material against one cheek, and her sisters looked—but somehow failed to see what a pleasing picture she made. She had just come in from shopping and had not yet removed her hat, and its trimming of foliage repeated the colors of her face—autumnal tints of red and bronze and healthy yellow. She, the eldest of the family and the only unmarried one, was forty-five, but she was rosy and fat and matronly, while her sisters were pinched and anemic. They were old maids by nature, she by chance.

"It becomes you well enough, but under the circumstances," Jane said, exchanging glances with Selina, "it seems a pity to buy all these things."

Mary Ann opened her eyes wide.

"Circumstances? What circumstances? It's no more than I buy every fall," protested the puzzled Mary Ann. "The flowered piece is for a morning wrapper, the tartan's for a street suit, and the blue-gray's a company dress."

Jane and Selina again exchanged glances, and Selina nodded.

"You never did seem to look ahead, Mary Ann," said Jane, thus encouraged. "I don't believe you realize that an attack of bronchitis is serious at ma's age. I wouldn't have got *all* my clothes colored. It's never any harm to have *one* black dress."

Mary Ann gasped. "Good gracious!" was all she said.

"Well, Mary Ann," said Selina, coming to Jane's rescue, "there's not a particle of use shutting your eyes to plain facts. Ma's in a serious condition, and if anything happens to her, what'll you do with all that stuff? You may dye the blue, but that tartan won't take a good black."

"Why," Mary Ann said, recovering speech, "ma has bronchitis at the beginning of cold weather every year. She'll be downstairs in a week or two, the same as she aways is."

"I hope so, Mary Ann. I hope, when next she comes down, it won't be feet first. But we're told to prepare for the worst while we hope for the best," said Jane solemnly, imagining that she was quoting scripture. "You and ma act as if there was nothing to prepare for. To see you sitting by her sick-bed, reading trashy love-stories out of the magazines, and both of you as much interested!—it gives me a creepy feeling."

"When my poor husband lay in his last illness," sighed Selina, "he was only too willing to be flattered into the belief that he was going to get well, but I wouldn't let him deceive himself, and it's a comfort to me now I didn't. I had everything ready but my crape when he died. I didn't have to depend on the neighbors for a dress for the funeral, as I've known some do."

"Many a time I've lent, but never borrowed," Jane boasted.

"And of course, never laying off widow's weeds, I'm ready for whatever comes." Selina stroked her tarlatan cuffs complacently, yet modestly withal, as if not wishing to make others feel too keenly the difference in their position.

Mary Ann gathered the dress goods together and threw them in a heap on the sofa. "There, I'm sorry I showed them to you," she cried; "you've got me almost turned against them. I declare, I'd be melancholy in two minutes more. Now you listen to me, Selina'n'Jane. There's no need to worry about ma's preparations for the next world; she's not thinking of leaving this world yet, and there's no reason why she should. The day you two go away, she'll be standing at the gate to say good-by to you, just the same as she always is. You see if she's not, Selina'n'Jane."

She left the room with something as like a flounce as her figure would permit. Stealing softly into the half-darkened bedroom at the head of the stairs, she stood looking down at the sleeping woman in the bed. The indignant moisture in her eyes turned to a mist of tenderness that blotted out the sight until a few drops formed and fell.

She was too unsuspicious to observe an unsleep-like flickering of the eyelids. She turned to tiptoe out of the room again. There was a quick peep, a look of relief, a husky whisper, "Is that you, Mary Ann?"

"Well now, I never did see anything like the regular way you wake up at medicine time," Mary Ann said, opening the shutters and consulting her watch. "Anybody'd think you had an alarm inside of you to go off at the right time."

She administered the dose and then went on with a cheerful monologue. She had got into this habit in the sick-room because her mother hated silence and had to save her own voice.

"What kept me so long was that everybody I met wanted to stop me and ask how you were. Everybody seemed pleased to hear you were getting along so nicely. Mrs. Dowling said Dr. Corbett told her you were the most satisfactory patient he had, because you always did everything he told you and always got well."

The sick woman smiled up at her. She had a smile that came and went easily, and Mary Ann had become skilful in the art of conducting a conversation in such a way that it served as well as words.

"And Caroline Sibbet said to tell you she was counting on going with us to the reception to the minister, and she didn't believe she'd go at all unless you were well by then."

It was a wistful smile now.

"So I told her she needn't be afraid, you'd be there."

A smile of appeal, as if to ask, "Do you really think so?"

Mary Ann gave her a puzzled glance. Something was wrong.

"Of course you'll be well by then, dearie. You heard what the doctor said to-day—that you might go back to having your cup of tea again to-morrow. That's always the first sign you're getting well, then you get leave to sit up. A week sitting up in your room, a week going downstairs—" Mary Ann began to check off the weeks on her fingers, but her mother interrupted.

"Was that Jane the doctor was talking to so long in the hall to-day?"

"Let me see. No, that was Selina."

"What was he saying to her?"

"He was saying every blessed thing that he's said to me since you took sick, and that I've repeated over again to her. But you know how it is with those two, ma. I believe they think there's some kind of magic in the marriage ceremony that gives a woman sense—they don't give me credit for a speck. When Selina told me she was going to speak to the doctor herself to-day, says she, 'You know that it stands to reason, Mary Ann, that you can't be as experienced as one that has been a wife five years and a widow seven'; and then Jane seemed to think it was being cast up to her that she wasn't a widow, so she speaks up real snappy, 'Nor one that's brought up a family of four boys,' and then Selina *she* looked mad."

Mary Ann went off into a peal of laughter at the remembrance.

"Jane told me he said at my age the heart was weak and there was always more or less danger."

"He always says that after he's told what good sound lungs you have, and what steady progress you're making, and how he'd rather pass you for insurance than most women half your age. It means we're not to be too reckless, all the same."

"She says if I *should* recover from this attack—"

"Sakes alive! Did she come over all that with you, too? 'If you should recover from this attack, you'd better sell the house and visit round among your married children?' Visit round as much as you like, ma, but have a house of your own to come back to; that's my advice."

"She said you wouldn't want to keep up a house after you were left alone—"

Mary Ann threw up her hands. "No wonder Selina'n'Jane are thin—they wear the flesh off their bones providing for the future. They're born Colquhouns. I'm glad I take after your side of the family. Do you know what Selina told me, ma? The preserves she put up this year won't have to be touched till winter after next. She has enough to last her over two years. 'Land sakes!' I said, 'what do you want to eat stale jam for, when you might have fresh?' The two get competing which will be furthest ahead in their work; from the way they talk, I shouldn't wonder if before long their fall house-cleaning would be done in the spring. It makes me think of what pa used to tell about his Uncle Alick Colquhoun—how he was earlier and earlier with the milking, till at last the evening milking was done in the morning, and the morning's was done the night before. Then there was Eva Meldrum; you remember she had all her marriage outfit ready before she was asked—sheets, tablecloths, and everything. As soon as Fred Healy proposed, she got right to work with the final preparations, and when she found herself left with nothing else to do—she just sat down and wrote out notes of thanks for the wedding gifts, leaving blanks for the names of the articles. I laughed till I was sore when she told me. 'You're a Colquhoun,' I said, 'though you do only get it from your grandma; you're a Colquhoun by nature if not by name.' You know I always say it comes from having such a name. It's enough to make an anxious streak in the family, having to spell it, one generation after another."

Mary Ann laughed so heartily that the sound reached her sisters, who wondered what "ma 'n' Mary Ann" were at now. And still the little cloud lingered, and the smile only flitted waveringly.

"I called at the library, ma, and brought home the magazine. Now we'll find out for sure whether Lady Geraldine marries the earl—I don't believe but what she's in love with the private secretary."

"Did you do the shopping?" her mother whispered.

"Yes, and if you feel rested with your sleep, I'll show you what I got. Mr. Merrill opened out such a heap of pretty things I didn't hardly know what to take. I was thinking, ma, it wouldn't be a bad idea to have Miss Adams in to sew, the first week you're downstairs, when we've got to be in the house anyway."

At that moment Jane and Selina came into the room to see what the sounds of merriment meant.

They looked at patient and nurse with disapproving gloom. Jane settled herself at once to her knitting; Selina, who never worked in the afternoon when she was wearing her widow's collars and cuffs, sat regarding her mother with an expression of grieved wonder. Mrs. Colquhoun was uncomfortably conscious of being judged by something in her own child of other heritage than hers—one of the strangest sensations a parent can have.

"You'd ought to keep quiet, ma," Selina said, after a prolonged scrutiny. "If you had any suitable book in the house, I'd read to you. There was one my poor husband used to listen to by the hour in his last illness—'Preparations for the Final Journey.' "

"I'm going to run down and fetch that stuff I bought to-day to show it to ma and get her opinion," Mary Ann interrupted, and a minute later she was standing by the bed with the three dress lengths piled in confusion upon her arms. To the woman in the bed it was as if an angel looked out from over a tumbled rainbow and smiled a message of hope to her from the sky.

"Take an end of this tartan, will you, Jane, and stand off a little with it. There, I knew you'd like it, ma. I said so to Mr. Merrill the minute he showed it to me. That flowered piece? That's for a morning wrapper. I know it's gay, but somehow, after the flowers are all over, I do hanker after gay colors. In summer I don't feel to want them so much on my back when I can have them in the garden. The gray-blue's for a company dress. I'll have it made up in time for the reception to the new minister. You'll need a dress for that, too, ma. We'll get samples as soon as you're well enough to choose. It was between this and a shot silk, but I thought this was more becoming at my age. To tell the truth," confessed Mary Ann with a laugh, "I'd rather have had it than this, and more than either I'd love to have bought me a dress off a piece of crimson velvet Mr. Merrill had just got in."

She rested an elbow on her knee and sank the length of a forefinger in her plump cheek.

"When I was a little girl," she ruminated, "I was awfully fond of the rose-in-campin' that grew in our garden at home—you mind it, mother; mullein pink, some call it. I used to say to myself that if ever I could get what clothes I liked, I'd have a dress as near like that as I could find. Well, there I was today looking at the very thing, the same color, the same downy look, and all, and money enough in my purse to buy it. Of course I know it would be silly. But don't it seem a pity that the things we dream of having some day—when the day comes, we don't want 'em? I feel somehow as if I'm cheating that little girl that wished for the dress like a rose-in-campin'."

She began to fold the pieces thoughtfully. "Made up handsomely with a train," she said, half to herself, "and worn on suitable occasions, it wouldn't seem so silly, either. I believe I'll have that crimson velvet yet," she concluded, with a laughing toss of the head. Her mother looked from the bright materials to the bright face above them.

"She would never have gone and bought all these colors just after the doctor said I wasn't going to get well," she thought, and turned over and fell into a real sleep. The last had been feigned—to escape Jane's disquieting remarks and to ponder their significance.

II

Mary Ann's prophecy was fulfilled. Her mother stood beside her at the garden gate when Jane and Selina drove away, her glances up and down the sunny street evincing all a convalescent's freshened interest in the outside world. The two faces were alike and yet unlike. The joy of living was in both but a little uncertainty, a little appeal in the older woman's told that with her it depended to some degree upon the steadier flow of animal spirits in the younger.

Jane and Selina turned for a last look at the portly figures and waving handkerchiefs.

"Who would think to look at them," said Jane, "that ma had only just returned from the jaws of death! It ought to be a warning to them. Some day she'll go off in one of those attacks."

"Ma'n'Mary Ann are as like as two peas," said Selina. "They're Maberlys. There never was a Maberly yet that knew how to look ahead. I declare, it gave me the shivers to see these two plunging right out of a sick-bed into colors and fashions the way they did. Ma'd ought to listen to us and sell her house and live round with her married children; at her age she'd ought to be some place where sickness and death are treated in a serious way."

Upon this point Mrs. Colquhoun was firm. She could never go back to life on a farm again, she said;

"living in town was *living*." But she compromised by agreeing to devote the whole of the next summer to visiting her married children.

That was a long summer to Mary Ann. There was something wanting in all the small accustomed pleasures of her simple life, until the middle of August came and the time set for the mother's return was within counting distance. Then her spirits rose higher and higher with every hour. As a toper would celebrate his happiness at the saloon, she went to Mr. Merrill's dry-goods shop, and after a revel in that part of it where color most ran riot, she bought new chintz covering for the parlor furniture, a chrysanthemum pattern in various shades of fawn and glowing crimson.

The next step was to plan a reception to welcome her mother home and exhibit the new covering. Then a mighty idea struck her—this was the opportunity for the crimson velvet dress!

"I mayn't never have as good an excuse for it again," she said to the sewing-girl, "and it's the one thing needed to make everything complete. Me in that crimson and ma in the fawn silk she had made when the Reverend Mr. Ellis came will be a perfect match for the furniture."

She patted the soft back with affectionate pride.

"It does make you feel good to have anything new," she said, sighing contentedly. "*Anything*, I don't care if it's only a kitchen stove-lifter. But this! There are an awful lot of things in the world do make you feel good; aren't there, Miss Adams? I mean common things, like putting on dry stockings when your feet are wet, or reading in bed, or sitting in a shady spot on a hot summer's day, with a muslin dress on—yes, or even eating your tea, if you happen to be feeling hungry and have something particularly nice," added this cheerful materialist.

The crimson velvet dress was being fitted for the last time when a letter was handed to Mary Ann. Her spectacles were downstairs, so she asked the sewing-girl to read it.

"'My dear aunt,'" Miss Adams began, "'Grandma took cold in church a week ago last Sunday and has been laid up—'"

There was a quick rustling of the velvet train. Mary Ann was vanishing into the clothes-closet. In a moment she reappeared with a small valise in her hand, and Miss Adams saw in her face what no one had ever seen there before—the shadow of a fear that hovered always on the outer edge of her happy existence and now stood close by her side. Mary Ann might be nine-tenths Maberly, but the other tenth was Colquhoun, after all.

"Put a dress into it, please," she said, handing the valise to Miss Adams. "No, I won't wait to take this off—I've a waterproof that will cover it all up. Pin the train up with safety pins—never mind if it does make pin-holes—I've just ten minutes to catch the train. *A week ago Sunday!* Oh, why didn't they let me know before?"

When she alighted from the train at the flag station she was clutching the waterproof close at the neck. She held it in the same unconscious grasp when she entered Jane's big farmhouse, by way of the kitchen. Selina was there, making a linseed poultice, and the odor was mingled with another which she knew afterward to be the odor of black dye.

In her mother's bedroom the same acid odor was in the air, and Jane was sitting at the window with a piece of black sewing in her hands. Jane's husband and John Maberly were standing at the foot of the bed, silent and melancholy, looking as awkward as men always do in a sick-room; Jane's stern gloom was tinged with a condescending pity for beings so out of place. Mary Ann saw them all at the first glance. Then she forgot everything; she was snuggling down against the bed, making the little, tender, glad, sorry sounds a mother makes when she has been separated from her baby.

When she lifted her head the men were leaving the room; John's face working. Selina was there with the poultice. She took it from her. One look into her mother's face had been enough. From that moment she seemed to be holding her back by sheer force of will from the edge over which she was slipping.

There was no merry gossip and laughter now, there were no love stories, no monologues with pauses for smiles. Mary Ann felt that a careless word or look would be enough to loosen that frail hold on life. When the doctor came he found his patient in charge of a stout woman in a fresh linen dress, whose self-command was so perfect that he did not waste many words in softening the opinion for which she followed him to the door.

"Your mother's age is against her," he said. "The bronchitis in itself is not alarming, but her heart is weak, and I fear you must not expect her recovery."

He knew at once that she refused to accept his verdict, though she only said, "I'd like to telegraph for our doctor at home, if you don't mind."

When Dr. Corbett came, he confirmed the opinion. "The bronchitis is no worse than usual," he added, "the treatment has been the same; but she seems to have lost her grip."

"There's no reason why she shouldn't catch a hold of it again," said poor Mary Ann, choking down her agony with the thought that she must return immediately to her mother's room.

"I don't quite understand it," the doctor said, with a questioning look. "The nursing—that's been good? Dr. Black tells me so."

"Yes, Jane and Selina are both good nurses, better'n what I am, if it wasn't that ma's used to me."

"And there's no obstacle to her recovery that you know of?" Mary Ann shook her head. "Well, Miss Mary Ann, we must just conclude that it's the natural wearing out of a good machine. And we'll do what we can."

When Mary Ann went back to her mother's room she found her a little roused from the stupor in which she had been lying. The visit of her own doctor, the accustomed attendance, had touched some spring that set old wheels running. With the clairvoyance love so often gives to the sick-nurse, Mary Ann knew that she had something to say to her.

She sat by the bed and waited. A fluttering whisper came at last.

"Did you see Jane's hands?"

Mary Ann's mind, seeking desperately for a clue, flashed from the stains on her sister's hands, which she had vaguely set down to black currant jelly, to the acid smell in the kitchen—to the black sewing—to the forgotten shock of a year ago.

"They asked me where I'd like to lie—beside pa or in the cemetery in town."

"It's their forehandedness, ma. I never did know such a forehanded pair. Talk about meeting trouble half way—Selina'n'Jane don't wait for it to start out at all."

"Selina read out of the paper that bronchitis was nearly always fatal after seventy."

"Well, now, what will those papers say next? Do you know what I read out of our own *Advertiser* the other day? That every woman over thirty has had at least one offer of marriage. Now, that's a lie, for I never had an offer in my life. I'm kind of glad I didn't, ma, for I suppose I'd have took it; and you and me do have an awfully good time together, don't we?"

But her mother was not listening now; it had been a flash merely of the old self. Mary Ann looked around the room until she found Jane's lap-board with a pile of black sewing on it. She gathered up the carefully pressed pieces and poked them roughly in between a large clothes cupboard and the wall.

"There!" she said to herself, "it will be a while before they find that, and when they do they can call it Mary Ann's flighty way of redding up a room."

She heard her sisters whispering in the hall and went out to them. Selina was tying her bonnet-strings.

"I'm going home to do a lot of cooking," she said in an important undertone. "John's wrote to ma's relatives in Iowa, and some of them's sure to come."

Mary Ann looked into the wrinkled face; the past weeks had added new lines of genuine grief to it, yet she could not help seeing that Selina found some strange pleasure in all these incidents of a last illness. The words she had meant to say seemed futile. She was turning to go into her mother's room again when an idea came to her.

"Don't go yet," she said. "I want to show you two something."

She went into her bedroom and returned in a few minutes with the crimson dress over her arm.

"I was getting it fitted when the news of ma's sickness came, and I just put a waterproof over it. The seams have got a little raveled. I thought maybe you two would help me to sew them."

"Mary Ann—!"

"You're so much cleverer than me with the needle. I was having it made for—for—" Mary Ann could not trust her voice to tell what she had been having it made for—"for an occasion. It won't be needed now as soon as I expected, but you know, Selina'n' Jane, you always say yourselves there's nothing like taking time by the forelock."

"Mary Ann—"

"A few hours would finish it up if we all got at it. Oh, there's ma coughing. I must run and get the pail of water and hot brick to steam up the room."

She threw the dress into her sister's hands and was gone. They stood looking at each other across it.

"*Poor* Mary Ann!"

"She talked about an occasion. I don't know

more'n one kind of occasion people get dresses like this for. Can she mean—?"

"At her age? Nonsense!"

"Dr. Corbett appears to think a pile of her. He's a widower—"

"Now you speak of it, Selina, he does look at her in an admiring sort of way. If there was anything of that kind in prospect—and of course she'd lay off black sooner—"

The sun came out and streamed through the high window upon the dress in their hands. It was like a drink of wine to look at it.

"There's no use denying it's a handsome thing," Jane said. "It does seem a pity to have the edges ravel. We might finish it, anyway, and sew it up in a bag with camphor."

Through the gray languor that overlay Mrs. Colquhoun's consciousness glints of crimson began to find their way. Now the spot of color was disappearing under Mary Ann's white apron; now it was in Jane's stained hands; now it was passing from Jane to Selina.

Then she heard Dr. Corbett say, as he handed Mary Ann a small parcel, "It's the first sewing-silk I ever bought, Miss Mary Ann, and I don't know whether it's a good match, but it's crimson, anyhow; Merrill gave me his word for that;" and when Mary Ann made a warning gesture toward the bed the faint stirring of interest almost amounted to curiosity.

"What did he mean?" she asked, after the doctor had gone. Mary Ann bent down to catch the husky whisper. "The silk—what is it for?"

"You're a little stronger to-day, aren't you, ma?

I've a secret I meant to keep till you were well; but there! Wait till I get back and I'll tell you."

Mrs. Colquhoun let her eyelids close and forgot all about it. When she opened them again Mary Ann stood before her arrayed in the velvet dress. The radiant vision seemed part of the train of visions that had been passing before her closed eyes; but this stayed, and the smiling creases of the cheeks were substantial and firm.

Then Mary Ann fell on her knees beside the bed and made a crimson frame of her arms for the night-capped head on the pillow.

"I'm not a bit of good at keeping a secret, ma. Jane and Selina and me have just finished it, but you weren't to know anything about it till you got home. It was to be a surprise. And there's new covering on the parlor furniture, a handsome flower pattern, all fawn and crimson, like our dresses, and we're going to have a home-coming party. I don't want to be impatient but I *wish* you'd hurry up and get well."

Mrs. Colquhoun was gazing into her daughter's eyes.

"Do you really think I'm going to get well, Mary Ann?" she asked, and the wistfulness of old desire revived was in the feeble voice.

"Of course you're going to get well, dearie. Why shouldn't you?"

"It seemed kind of settled I wasn't—and it's so upsetting to stay when you're expected to go. I didn't care much."

She put up her hand weakly and stroked the velvet.

"But now—if you think so—perhaps—"

At his next visit Dr. Corbett said, "Your mother's

caught her grip again, Miss Mary Ann," and Dr. Black added heartily, "And if you'll only tell us *how* you did it, Miss Mary Ann, you'll be putting dollars in our pockets."

But the cunning of love, with all its turnings and twistings, is only half-conscious—the rest is instinct.

"I don't know that there's anything to tell, doctor," Mary Ann said slowly, wiping away a tear. "Only you might just keep a watch out and see that none of your patients are being hurried out of the world by the preparations for their own mourning. That's what was happening to ma."

HENRY PEASLEE AND HIS AUNT EMMA

BY SARAH N. CLEGHORN

HENRY PEASLEE AND HIS AUNT EMMA

BY SARAH N. CLEGHORN

LITTLE Henry Peaslee, in his white pantaloons and purple roundabout, was amusing himself in the parlor as best he could. He examined the Chinese work-box with all its ivory shuttles and bobbins, the melon-seed bags and painted lambrequin; or else he watched the derrick swing large blocks of marble that looked no bigger than white beans in the mountain quarries far above.

In the sitting-room, in the other wing, his uncle and aunts were having a discussion as to which of them should take him to bring up. His Aunt Sarah said that she was perfectly willing to assume the responsibility. It would be a good deal of care, she said, but she would do her best to turn him out a good boy, and a healthy boy, and an industrious boy.

His Uncle Zadok shifted his mighty bulk in his chair.

"The little toad," said he, "had better come to us. Wife told me to fetch him home with me. 'Fetch him back here,' said she, 'and set him down among our children.' The more the merrier," concluded Henry's Uncle Zadok, whose sun-like face, fringed round by gray stubble, beamed like a paterfamilias in an allegorical picture.

But Henry's Aunt Emma said, in a trembling voice, while all her thin body shook:

"I want him! I crave after him, Sister Sarah—Brother Zadok!"

The others looked at her and at each other.

"Well," said Mrs. Sarah.

"Well," said Mr. Zadok a little doubtfully, "I'm—I'm agreed."

They drummed on the arms of their chairs a little longer, and rolled a glance or two round the ceiling, and wondered in their own minds whether poor Emma could really make a success of bringing up her orphaned nephew.

But her lap seemed to be waiting for him; her long arms looked empty; and the words that she had spoken vibrated still in the room.

"Well, Emma," said Mr. Zadok at length, "you've cut out quite a piece of work for yourself. I hope the boy'll be a comfort to ye. But let me give ye one piece of advice: make a man of him."

"Yes, Emma!" cried her sister. "Henry's a timid child, and you must harden him. You must toughen him."

Mr. Zadok nodded.

"Toughen him," repeated he. "Push him out to play with other boys. If he tumbles down and scrapes his nose, don't let him run to you a-bawling. Don't let him grow up afeared of dogs. Don't set by his bed to keep away the bogyman."

"But she will!" cried Mrs. Smith.

Miss Emma blushed.

"Well, enough said," concluded Mr. Zadok. Enough has been said to change all the echoes in the room, which before had been full of Miss Emma's "I crave after him!" but now were full of Mr. Zadok's "Make a man of him!"

It was quite true that Henry Peaslee was a nervous, timid, imaginative child. He started at sudden noises; he was afraid of dogs, and even of large cats; and often he had bad dreams, and woke up crying. He was an only child, with the blood of generations of introspective ministers flowing in his veins.

Now his maiden aunt, with a proprietary air, tied on his little circular cloak, and had scarcely hooked herself up in her own dolman when the Peru stage came bumping down the hill, and hawed to a stop between the giant locusts. Mr. Zadok escorted Miss Emma, and Mrs. Sarah lifted in the little boy; and the lean horses jogged away toward the sunset notch between Blueberry and Bald Fowl Mountains. And as the happy aunt, under cover of the kind canvas flap, stole her long arm round the boy, Mrs. Sarah was saying to Mr. Zadok in the house behind them:

"Emma Peaslee is no woman to bring up such a boy as Henry."

"No," said Mr. Zadok. "She wun't make a man of him."

Meantime the stage, slowly rolling over spur after spur of the mountains, came at length to "Sandacre Street," and took on another passenger from the store there. Henry felt a knocking in his ribs as the stranger entered. He was a hairy, gipsy-looking man, with earrings in his ears. As he sat down he stretched out his legs, like a board fence, across the stage, balancing the heel of one boot on the toe of the other. Henry hitched himself closer to his aunt. The stranger began poking with his stick in the dark corners of the stage, as if he had seen a rat. Henry clasped his aunt's arm, and huddled to her side. What was this fluttering beneath his ear? It was his Aunt Emma's heart palpitating like a rabbit's or a chipmunk's. Henry was amazed. Grown-up people, in his experience, had never been afraid—they were his protectors and protectresses. But here was his Aunt Emma breathing fast and short, and her hand was cold against his leg in its linen pantaloon!

They had reached the bad roads of Farnumville, and now, as one wheel went over a log, the other down in a mud pot, the gipsy, stick and all, was pitched violently against Miss Emma Peaslee and her nephew. Henry was all ready to cry; he felt the tears rising in his throat—tears which he tried in vain to swallow; but before they quite gushed out, his Aunt Emma, clutching him tightly, let out a faint shriek, and followed it with a hundred tiny panting breaths.

And then there awoke and stirred in Henry Peaslee's soul a feeble, blind impulse of chivalry, no bigger than a moth-miller. It fluttered about inside of him, and filled him with a curious discomfort. His chest felt hot. He turned his face off his aunt's bosom, and looked at the stranger, who had sunk deep into his loose coat. Ah! he was a terrible-looking customer. His front teeth bit into his lower lip; his hairy neck, his knotty hands made him look wild and fierce. But Henry's blood was up since he had heard his aunt's tender little scream. He turned to the fierce mountaineer; he opened his mouth, and, trembling all over, thrust out his tongue at him.

"You did-did-dasn't bump into my auntie again!" said he in a brave, quavering voice. And immediately a little man stood up inside of him and made him feel big enough to pitch the gipsy out over the back wheels.

"Here we air, little nephew! Here we air in Farnumville, and this is the little green house where we belong!"

It was late in the winter of that (to Miss Emma Peaslee) ever memorable year that her brother and sister at last succeeded in getting over to Farnumville to see her. The visit had long been talked of, but the heat, the cold, and the rain had intervened; Zadok had shingles and Sarah a touch of gout; and mud and drifts prevented the stage from making its circuit. But at length, on a day late in February, Henry's uncle and his Aunt Sarah descended from the stage at the post-office, and walked down the long, marble street to the little green house.

"I hope Emma will be to home," said Mr. Zadok, thinking of his sister's currant shrub.

Mrs. Sarah smiled.

"She's probably at home, teaching Henry to do his patchwork," said she.

"Or dressing a dolly for him," added Mr. Zadok.

"Or tying his hair up with a blue ribbon," said Mrs. Sarah.

"Poor little toad!" said Mr. Zadok, "setting to home with his auntie on a Saturday afternoon! Or if she takes him out, it'll be to call on the minister— Whifkachoo! who throwed that slushball, boys? Which of ye done it?"

"Ah! that catched ye plumb on the ear, mister," chuckled an aged man in the doorway of a store.

"Which of ye done it?" repeated Mr. Zadok, glaring at the boys within a fort of snow across the street. The soggy ball had splashed his spectacles and dickey, and was trickling down his shoulder-blade.

"I can tell ye who throwed it," said the aged bystander. "It was that young one in the plum-colored roundabout. I don't recomember his name. He's full of all sech monkey-shines."

"Wal," roared Mr. Zadok, "if he dast to do sech a trick again, I'll come over thar and tan him. Who did ye say the little blackguard was? I can't see nothing through these spectacles, consarn the boy!"

"His name's kind of got away from me. It's some sort of gardin' truck, like Beans or Parsnip. He's a tough little feller. He's be'n out there sence the forenon, pluggin' every man that went by. He don't plug the ladies. Your company needn't have run away."

"Why, where *is* Sarey?" asked Mr. Zadok, looking round him. Mrs. Sarah had fled. Her blue barege skirt at that moment whisked into an alley and was lost to view.

"That little feller has blossomed out wonderful since he was fetched here by his auntie," volunteered the old man. "He was a pindlin', fidgety child. Naow he's the manliest little shaver you ever see. Oh, I recomember his name now—it's Peaslee. His folks was from Perew-way."

Mr. Zadok caught the old man by the sleeve.

"Manly little shaver, is he?" he asked eagerly.

"Wal, I guess yes! Why, here a while ago the gipsies stole his auntie's old Speckler, the best layin' hen she had. What did that little feller do, hey? Why, he took after the gipsy wagon, follered it out of taown to the old sand-bank, and hung around their camp till dark, and got hold of the old hen, and fetched her hum."

"By a rabbit!" cried Mr. Zadok, slapping his giant thigh.

"By a rabbit, hey? That hain't a circumstance. Here in the fall they had a torchlight parade for Franklin Pierce. That little Pa'snip feller he clumb out of his winder, after his auntie had put him to bed and blowed out his candle; he shinned down the old popple-tree, and run up to the church and rung the bell like sixty-seven!"

"Good for the little tyke!" shouted Mr. Zadok, thumping his new friend on the shoulder.

"I see you know the p'ints of a boy," said the old man gleefully, though his shoulder was sore.

"I ought to know the p'ints of this one," said Mr. Zadok, "for he's my brother Alferd's son."

"You don't tell me that!"

"I do," said Mr. Zadok, swelling out his chest with pride.

"Wal, sir!"

"Yes, sir! But when I knowed him, he was sech a pindlin', fidgety child as you describe. What's made this mighty change in him, hey?"

"You want me to tell ye, mister?"

"I do, sir."

"Wal, sir, look across the street thar. That's his auntie."

Mr. Zadok looked. Through the shouting, snowballing group of boys, he could see his sister Emma's delicate, thin form, clad in her calling dress of watered silk, and Paisley shawl. She was cowering on the curbstone, with both arms up as if to shield her head. She took a step forward, then retreated three; and was hovering still on the curb when she caught sight of Henry's purple roundabout, and forthwith began to call in a faint voice:

"Nenny! Nenny! Nenny!"

"Look at the little feller now, mister."

Mr. Zadok looked, and saw his young nephew scramble to his feet and tear hot-foot across the street. He gave his aunt his arm with a most Chesterfieldian air; and she clung to him as if he were a captain of marines. And Henry looked the part. His shoulders were thrown back, and he walked with a mighty swagger. Not one of his late companions threw a slushball at him, as he escorted his lady aunt across the street.

"Wal," said Mr. Zadok, "I'm beat. This is too many for me."

"Brother! You here!" cried Miss Emma.

Mr. Zadok hardly heard. He was patting his nephew on the head, the shoulders, and the back. He had no thoughts for any one else, for as the antediluvian in the store doorway had said, Mr. Zadok was a connoisseur in boys.

"You was quite a little man, thar, son," said he. "Your auntie hain't spoiled you yit. I want you should come over to South Derry and visit my boys. Thar's Fred, is ten, and Josiph, eight, and William—"

"Wha-what say, Brother Zadok?" cried Miss Emma

Peaslee, all in a flutter, laying her thin fingers on her brother's arm. "What air you saying to Nenny?"

Mrs. Sarah was peering out of her alley. She heard her brother Zadok repeat:

"Why, I want the little tyke should come and spend a week with our boys, over to South Derry."

And then she heard her sister Emma reply:

"Oh, brother! You're very kind. But I can't spare him. You won't go away and leave auntie, will you, Nenny?" She was fluttering, and almost crying.

"No, ma'am, I wun't—I never will!" cried the little boy.

"I'm most afraid to go for the milk without Nenny," resumed Miss Emma. "He purtects me from that fierce cow of the Snookses. I like him with me, too, when his grandfather's gun has to be dusted. And to tell the truth, brother, I—I don't know how I could go to sleep at night without Nenny looked under my bed, to—to see, you know, brother—if there was a—a man there." When Miss Emma had thus spoken, her sister Sarah and her brother Zadok both began to realize with wonder and admiration how their timid sister, in her old-fashioned, womanly, and quite unconscious way, had made a man of little Henry.

SCRAP

BY LUCIA CHAMBERLAIN

SCRAP

BY LUCIA CHAMBERLAIN

AT the gray end of afternoon the regiment, twelve companies, went through Monterey on its way to the summer camp, a mile out on the salt-meadows; and it was here that Scrap joined it.

He did not tag at the heels of the boys who tagged the last company, or rush out with the other dogs who barked at the band; but he appeared, somehow independent of any surroundings, and marched, ears alert, stump tail erect, one foot in front of the tall first lieutenant who walked on the wing of Company A.

The lieutenant was self-conscious and so fresh to the service that his shoulder-straps hurt him. He failed to see Scrap, who was very small and very yellow, until, in quickening step, he stumbled over him and all but measured his long length. He aimed an accurate kick that sent Scrap flying, surprised but not vindictive, to the side lines, where he considered, his head cocked. With the scratched ear pricked and the bitten ear flat, he passed the regiment in review until Company K, with old Muldoon sergeant on the flank, came by.

As lean, as mongrel, as tough, and as scarred as Scrap, he carried his wiry body with a devil-may-care assurance, in which Scrap may have recognized a kindred spirit. He decided in a flash. He made a dart and fell in abreast the sergeant of Company K. Muldoon saw and growled at him.

"Gr-r-r-r!" said Scrap, not ill-naturedly, and fell back a pace. But he did not slink. He had the secret of success. He kept as close as he could and yet escape Muldoon's boot. With his head high, ears stiff, tail up, he stepped out to the music.

Muldoon looked back with a threat that sent Scrap retreating, heels over ears. The sergeant was satisfied that the dog had gone; but when camp was reached and ranks were broken he found himself confronted by a disreputable yellow cur with a ragged ear cocked over his nose.

"Well, I'm domned!" said Muldoon. His heart, probably the toughest thing about him, was touched by this fearless persistence.

"Ar-ren't ye afraid o' nothin', ye little scrap?" he said. Scrap, answering the first name he had ever known, barked shrilly.

"What's that dog doing here?" said the tall lieutenant of Company A, disapprovingly.

"I'm afther kickin' him out, sor," explained Muldoon, and, upon the lieutenant's departure, was seen retreating in the direction of the cook-tent, with the meager and expectant Scrap inconspicuously at his heels.

He went to sleep at taps in Muldoon's tent, curled up inside Muldoon's cartridge-belt; but at reveille the next morning the sergeant missed him. Between drill and drill Muldoon sought diligently, with insinuations as to the character of dog-stealers that were near to precipitating personal conflict. He found the stray finally, in Company B street, leaping for bones amid the applause of the habitants. Arraigned collectively as thieves, Company B declared that the dog had strayed in and remained only because he could not be kicked out. But their pride in the height of his leaps was too evidently the pride of possession; and Muldoon, after vain attempts to catch the excited Scrap, who was eager only for bones, retired with threats of some vague disaster to befall Company B the next day if *his* dog were not returned.

The responsibility, with its consequences, was taken out of Company B's hands by Scrap's departure from their lines immediately after supper. He was not seen to go. He slid away silently among the broken shadows of the tents. Company B reviled Muldoon. Scrap spent the night in a bugler's cape, among a wilderness of brasses, and reappeared the next morning at guard mount, deftly following the stately maneuvers of the band.

"Talk about a dorg's gratitude!" said the sergeant of Company B, bitterly, remembering Scrap's entertainment of the previous evening.

"I'm on his game!" muttered old Muldoon. "Don't ye see, ye fool, he don't belong to any *wan* of us. He belongs to the crowd—to the regiment. That's what he's tryin' to show us. He's what that Frinchman down in F calls a—a mascot; and, be jabers, he moves like a soldier!"

The regiment's enthusiasm for Scrap, as voiced by Muldoon, was not extended to the commanding officer, who felt that the impressiveness of guard mount was detracted from by Scrap's deployments. Also the tall lieutenant of Company A disliked the sensation of being accompanied in his social excursions among ladies who had driven out to band practise by a lawless yellow pup with a bitten ear. The lieutenant, good fellow at bottom, was yet a bit of a snob, and he would have preferred the colonel's foolish Newfoundland to the spirited but unregenerate Scrap.

But the privates and "non-coms" judged by the spirit, and bid for the favor of their favorite, and lost money at canteen on the next company to be distinguished as Scrap's temporary entertainers. He was cordial, even demonstrative, but royally impartial, devoting a day to a company with a method that was military. He had personal friends,—Muldoon for one, the cook for another,—but there was no man in the regiment who could expect Scrap to run to his whistle.

Yet independent as he was of individuals, he obeyed regimental regulations like a soldier. He learned the guns and the bugles, what actions were signified by certain sounds. He was up in the morning with the roll of the drums. He was with every drill that was informal enough not to require the presence of the commanding officer, and during dress parade languished, lamenting, in Muldoon's tent. Barking furiously, he was the most enthusiastic spectator of target practise. He learned to find the straying balls when the regimental nine practised during "release," and betrayed a frantic desire to "retrieve" the shot that went crashing seaward from the sullen-mouthed cannon on the shore. More than once he made one of the company that crossed the lines at an unlawful hour to spend a night among the crooked ways of Monterey.

The regiment was tiresome with tales of his tricks.

The height of his highest leap was registered in the mess, and the number of rats that had died in his teeth were an ever increasing score in the canteen. He was fairly aquiver with the mere excitement and curiosity of living. There was no spot in the camp too secure or too sacred for Scrap to penetrate. His invasions were without impertinence; but the regiment was his, and he deposited dead rats in the lieutenant's shoes as casually as he concealed bones in the French horn; and slumbered in the major's hat-box with the same equanimity with which he slept in Muldoon's jacket.

The major evicted Scrap violently, but, being a good-natured man, said nothing to the colonel, who was not. But it happened, only a day after the episode of the hat-box, that the colonel entered his quarters to find the yellow mascot, fresh from a plunge in the surf and a roll in the dirt, reposing on his overcoat.

To say that the colonel was angry would be weak; but, overwhelmed as he was, he managed to find words and deeds. Scrap fled with a sharp yelp as a boot-tree caught him just above the tail.

His exit did not fail to attract attention in the company street. The men were uneasy, for the colonel was noticeably a man of action as well as of temper. Their premonitions were fulfilled when, at assembly the next morning, an official announcement was read to the attentive regiment. The colonel, who was a strategist as well as a fighter, had considered the matter more calmly overnight. He was annoyed by the multiplicity of Scrap's appearances at times and places where he was officially a nuisance. He was more than annoyed by the local paper's recent reference to "our crack yellow-dog regiment." But he knew the strength of regimental sentiment concerning Scrap and the military superstition of the mascot, and he did not want to harrow the feelings of the "summer camp" by detailing a firing squad. Therefore he left a loophole for Scrap's escape alive. The announcement read: "All dogs found in camp not wearing collars will be shot, by order of the commanding officer."

Now there were but two dogs in camp, and the colonel's wore a collar. The regiment heard the order with consternation.

"That'll fix it," said the colonel, comfortably.

"Suppose some one gets a collar?" suggested the major, with a hint of hopefulness in his voice.

"I know my regiment," said the colonel. "There isn't enough money in it three days before pay day to buy a button. They'll send him out to-night."

Immediately after drill there was a council of war in Muldoon's tent, Muldoon holding Scrap between his knees. Scrap's scratched ear, which habitually stood cocked, flopped forlornly; his stump tail drooped dismally. The atmosphere of anxiety oppressed his sensitive spirit. He desired to play, and Muldoon only sat and rolled his argumentative tongue. From this conference those who had been present went about the business of the day with a preternatural gloom that gradually permeated the regiment. The business of the day was varied, since the next day was to be a field day, with a review in the morning and cavalry maneuvers in the afternoon.

All day Scrap was conspicuous in every quarter of the camp, but at supper-time the lieutenant of Company A noted his absence from his habitual place at the left of Muldoon in the men's mess-tent. The lieutenant was annoyed by his own anxiety.

"Of course they'll get him out, sir?" he said to the major.

"Of course," the major assented, with more confidence than he felt. The colonel was fairly irritable in his uncertainty over it.

Next morning the sentries, who had been most strictly enjoined to vigilant observation, reported that no one had left camp that night, though a man on beat four must have failed in an extraordinary way to see a private crossing his line six feet in front of him.

The muster failed to produce any rag-eared, stub-tailed, eager-eyed, collarless yellow cub. Nor did the mess-call raise his shrill bark in the vicinity of the cook's tent. The lieutenant felt disappointed. He thought that the regiment should at least have made some sort of demonstration in Scrap's defense. It seemed a poor return for such confidence and loyalty to be hustled out of the way on an official threat.

It seemed to him the regiment was infernally light-hearted, as, pipe-clay white and nickel bright in the morning sun, it swung out of camp for the parade-ground, where the dog-carts and runabouts and automobiles were gathering from Del Monte and the cottage along the shore.

The sight of the twelve companies moving across the field with the step of one warmed the cockles of the colonel's pride. The regiment came to parade rest, and the band went swinging past their front, past the reviewing-stand. As it wheeled into place, the colonel, who had been speaking to the adjutant, who was the lieutenant of Company A, bit his sentence in the middle, and glared at something that moved, glittering, at the heels of the drum-major.

The colonel turned bright red. His glass fell out of his eye-socket.

"What the devil is the matter with that dog?" he whispered softly. And the adjutant, who had also seen and was suffocating, managed to articulate, "Collars!"

The colonel put his glass back in his eye. His shoulders shook. He coughed violently as he addressed the adjutant:

"Have that dog removed—no, let him alone—no, adjutant, bring him here!"

So the adjutant, biting his lip, motioned Muldoon to fall out.

Tough old Muldoon tucked Scrap, struggling, squirming, glittering like a hardware-shop, under his arm, and saluted his commander, while the review waited.

The colonel was blinking through his glass and trying not to grin.

"Sergeant, how many collars has that dog got on?"

"Thirteen, sor," said Muldoon.

"What for?" said the colonel, severely.

"Wan for each company, sor, an' wan for the band."

THE AMATEUR SKIPPER

BY BERT LESTON TAYLOR

THE AMATEUR SKIPPER

BY BERT LESTON TAYLOR

CHARACTERS

LOVEST, *the Amateur Skipper*
SWEETHEART, *his wife*
GEORGE, *their long-suffering friend*
MR. TIMBY, *a landlubber*
MISS WILKINS, *a lady landlubber*

WHEN George rowed us over the bright blue sea to the good yawl *Cauliflower,* the Amateur Skipper and his wife were untying the stops of the mainsail. The jib and jigger were already set, and, in my landlubberly judgment, any further spread of duck held promise of a ducking, for it was blowing two-thirds of a gale out of the east, and Neptune's white ponies were kicking up their heels outside.

"Good sailing breeze," I remarked conventionally to George. Anything short of a typhoon comes under the head of a good sailing breeze.

"Fine," replied George. "Beam ends for Bilger to-day."

Personally, I am not keen for beam ends. Like honest Gonzalo, I would fain die a dry death. Give me a ten-foot skiff with a leg-of-mutton sail, a gentle breeze, and a bathing suit, and I don't care what happens—I am indifferent to danger to the point of recklessness; but when I put forth in a thirty-foot yawl, with an amateur skipper and a landscape artist for a crew, I prefer a dry sheet to a wet one, and am no fonder of a "snoring breeze" than of a snoring drummer in a sleeping-car.

"So glad you could come," said Mrs. Bilger sweetly, as she hauled us aboard the *Cauliflower*. The Amateur Skipper looked up from his work and nodded cordially. "How are you, Timby?" said he. "Great day for a sail, isn't it?" His eyes were bright as were the Ancient Mariner's. The prospect of putting the cabin windows under water flooded his strenuous soul with anticipatory delight.

George was instructed to make the dingey fast astern. "We're going to drag it," said Bilger. For the enlightenment of the unnautical it should be said that a dingey or other small boat is always "dragged" —never in any circumstances towed.

"Lively now, George," said the Skipper. "Let's get the mainsail up. Peak-halyards, old man."

George had three guesses at the peak-halyards, and finally got hold of them; and while the mainsail was going up, we landlubbers—

(But I beg pardon, Reader: you have not met Miss Wilkins. Miss Wilkins, may I present Mr. Reader? You know the Readers—a very large and interested family.)

We landlubbers stowed ourselves aft, in a welter of ropes, and Mrs. Bilger relieved our minds of any doubts we may have entertained concerning the stanchness of the good yawl *Cauliflower*. I gathered that she was built on the conservative lines of a cyclone-cellar; it was impossible to capsize her; she would accept a knock-down as cheerfully as a pugilist, and bob up serenely before one could count ten. Truth crushed to earth rose not more inevitably.

While we were absorbing these comforting details, Miss Wilkins suddenly clutched my arm to avoid going over the side; at the same moment there came a sound of ripping canvas. An uncommonly violent gust had slammed against the wall of the spread mainsail, and as the main-sheet had not been cast off, nor even slackened, the yawl, still at her mooring, heeled over. Something had to give, and the mainsail tore at a place which, I later ascertained, is called the clew.

"Oh, Lovest, what a shame!" exclaimed Mrs. Bilger, her heart in her voice.

"Tore out the grommets!" said the Skipper, in hollow tones.

"Grommets! What a funny word!" said Miss Wilkins.

"Yes," said George, with a jarring levity; "sounds like something for an English breakfast, toasted and buttered, doesn't it?"

"Drop it, George," said Bilger dismally, referring to the mainsail. "We'll have to go out under the jib and jigger."

I murmured my regrets, but they were insincere, hollow as a popover. Secretly I was not sorry that the big sail had been put out of commission. The danger of an upset was now reduced to a minimum.

"Which is the jib?" Miss Wilkins asked me. I pointed it out and explained its unique function, which is to aid and abet the mainsail. "And that funny little hindsail—that must be the jigger," she pursued. "I supposed a jigger was something used in mixing cocktails. My brother has one."

I assured Miss Wilkins that her supposition and her brother were correct; but there are jiggers and jiggers, not counting the insect that makes its lair beneath the human skin. One speaks of a jigger of gin: why not a jigger of wind? "The jigger-sail," said I, first ascertaining that Mrs. Bilger was not listening, "is so called because it holds a measured quantity of wind."

"How interesting!" murmured Miss Wilkins. "Nautical terms are perfectly fascinating, aren't they?"

I remarked that the terminology of sailing was by far its most interesting feature, and we stood up to watch George slip the mooring.

I hope that phrase is correct; it clinks well. I remember reading not long ago, in one of our smartest metropolitan journals, of a battleship that "weighed and slipped her anchor"—a feat as difficult of accomplishment as to eat your cake and have it. Now Neptune preserve me from such a paradox! But it is easier to gibe at the blunders of others than to be nautically correct oneself.

George gaily tossed the tin buoy overboard and the Amateur Skipper took the wheel.

"Start the engine, Sweetheart," he instructed.

"Yes, Lovest," replied Mrs. Bilger, and disappeared below.

We were informed that it was necessary to use the gasoline auxiliary because the channel was so narrow.

The engine chugged responsive.

"Why, I don't believe we are moving," said Miss Wilkins, peering over the side.

Nor were we. George had heaved overboard the buoy with the small rope attached, but the hawser was still catted.

"You're a great sailor, George," Bilger observed in good-natured contempt. George laughed shamelessly.

As a matter of fact, he was no sailor at all, but a landscape artist. Devoted to art for art's sake, he cared nothing for sailing for sailing's sake. He appreciated certain poetical features of sailing, which are to be observed in the golden mean between a hurricane and a flat calm; but sailing *per se* interested him no more than sawing wood, or washing dishes, or automobiling through a landscape at forty miles an hour. But George was amiable and long-suffering; he was one of those rare spirits that an amateur skipper too infrequently happens on—a friend who will suppress a groan when asked if he would like to go a-sailing, and answer: "Why, yes, I'd be delighted."

The engine stopped abruptly of its own accord, as commonly auxiliaries will; but we cleared the channel and began to bump the ground-swell bumps with our decks at an angle of forty-five degrees.

"The jig and jigger do very well, don't they?" said Miss Wilkins, as we retreated to the main-hatch to keep our feet out of the wet. "What a lot of ropes. I suppose they all have names."

"How many ropes," spoke up the Skipper, who was enjoying a moment of leisure, "how many ropes do you suppose there are on the biggest sailing ship afloat?"

I started the guessing match at a hundred. George

doubled the number. Miss Wilkins was sure there must be at least a thousand.

"Only four," said the Skipper: "the man-rope, the foot-rope, the bucket-rope, and, occasionally, the mast-rope. All the other hemp things are called halyards, sheets, braces, stays, guys, lines, tacks, clew-garnets, spanker-vangs, downhauls, and so on."

"There's wisdom while you wait!" said George, who was coiling about a quarter of a mile of main-sheet.

Miss Wilkins turned to me: "How many hemp hings do *you* know, Mr. Timby?"

"Only one—the jib-downhaul," I replied modestly.

But I am strong on the jib-downhaul. You will observe me grasping it firmly as we approach a mooring. The man with the boat-hook is nervous; he is afraid he will miss the mooring, and he usually does. The skipper's nerves are taut as fiddle-strings; he has no confidence in the man with the boat-hook. I alone am imperturbable. "Jib-downhaul!" is my cue. Four or five yeo-ho yanks, and the jib is in the water, from which the skipper, cursing softly, later extricates it. In all my sailing I do not think that I have once missed putting the jib in the water.

"George," called the Amateur Skipper, "will you take one more pull on the jib-halyard?" George hastened forward. "Trim the jigger-sheet, sweetheart." Mrs. Bilger braced herself against the cockpit wall and hauled.

"Mrs. Bilger is a sweet little woman, isn't she?" whispered Miss Wilkins, as we balanced ourselves atop the furled mainsail and spread a raincoat over our knees.

"Sweet as they come," I agreed, and observed that Mr. Bilger was a remarkable skipper. For I know dilettante mariners, the most amiable men ashore, whose natures seem to undergo a sharp change the instant that they tread the decks of their obsessions. They become imperative; their tempers shorten to pie-crust brittleness; they treat their wives shamefully. But Bilger, beyond a certain nervous tension and a staccato manner of speaking, behaved very well; and Mrs. Bilger was the most obedient and uncomplaining of helpmeets. Some of the tasks he laid upon her seemed beyond her strength, for she was a frail little woman; but if Bilger were to say, "Sweetheart, fetch up the five-hundred-pound anchor," she would hasten below, and presently her cheerful voice would be heard: "Coming, Lovest, and this isn't a bit heavy."

The outward run of the good yawl *Cauliflower,* with the wind abeam, consumed two hours; and from the view-point of the Amateur Skipper it may have been a most exciting trip; he was as busy as a puppy chasing an autumn leaf, and he communicated his feverish activity to George and Mrs. Bilger. But from my limited view-point there was only a slosh of sea-water.

Yachting is a pastime for the well-to-do; but any one may have the pleasures of it and still remain ashore. All you need do is don a yachting cap and to sit on a soap box and have somebody throw water on your feet, with now and then a pailful in your lap; that will do nicely for hard-weather sailing. For the other sort you may sit on a wooden bench in a hot sun and tie knots in a clothesline.

When the *Cauliflower* rounded the lee of Gooseberry Island, I, for one, was glad of the chance to go ashore and stretch my legs. Mrs. Bilger took along the afternoon-tea things, and we sipped the wine of Ceylon in a breathless nook in an angle of the cliff. It was wholly pleasant. I could have stood it for several hours. And the artist soul of George was steeped in content.

But the Amateur Skipper was restless. After one cup of tea and a bite at a biscuit he was back on the yawl, puttering about above and below, fussing with the hemp things and squinting learnedly at the sky.

Bilger's fad possessed him utterly. He could work a lunar observation, calculate an azimuth, find the arithmetical complement of a logarithm, build a sea-anchor, and tie all manner of recondite knots; and there was not a drop of salt water in his veins. Calmly ecstatic, he would talk sailing by the hour, or day, or week. Ask him what a "grommet" might be and his eye would light up and roll in a fine frenzy. Inquire politely as to the meaning of the occult term "leech," and you had leech and luff, head and foot, peak and throat, clew and tack, explained to you in one breath. Bilger's heart was in his yawl; his mind was concentered on his mainsail's weather-edge; he thought in reaches; his soul was forever beating to windward.

"What does Mr. Bilger do in winter?" inquired Miss Wilkins, passing her cup.

"He talks of going south for a cruise," said Mrs. Bilger; "but I always discourage the idea. Mr. Bilger needs to rest a few months. He gets so dreadfully thin in summer."

At this point the emaciated Bilger returned to our tea-party to announce that it was high time we were starting homeward; the wind was dropping. We rose reluctantly.

The wind was not only dropping, but it had hauled into the north; and we made little progress beating up with only the "jig and jibber," as Miss Wilkins persisted in calling them, drawing. Bilger started in to repair the torn mainsail, but the wind was running out like tide-water and with sunset the last zephyr expired. The *Cauliflower* lay as idle as a painted ship upon a playhouse curtain.

"You'll have to start the engine, George," said the skipper. "Careful of your hand, old man; she may reverse on you."

But nothing so exciting happened. "She" declined to start, though George toiled over her like Sisyphus over his stone. From the sulphurous haze that began to fog the hatchway I knew that George was breathing out profanity with every futile revolution of the fly-wheel. Dr. Bilger made a diagnosis which revealed the fact that the engine was flooded. Precisely what this meant he explained, with a wealth of technical detail.

"Suppose," I suggested to George, "that you and I row the dingey and tow the yawl."

"Good idea," the Skipper answered for him. "You fellows go ahead, and I'll see what I can do with the engine."

And so it was ordered.

"This," remarked George, after we had pulled for half an hour with none too encouraging results, "this is something like towing a brick-yard."

"At least," said I, "we are getting some action. Not much plot or heart-interest as yet, but you can't tell what may develop."

"I'm glad to get off the yawl, at least," George confided in an undertone, for the ladies were sitting forward, watching our back-breaking labors. "Every time I go out with Bilger I swear it will be the last; but I never have the heart to refuse him—he's a good soul. But he'll have to shanghai me after this." He dropped his oars to fire a pipe. "The first cruise I took on the *Cauliflower,*" he pursued reminiscently, "she was bran-new, and she leaked like a landing-net. I had to bail for three mortal hours, with the water in the cabin up to my knees. Now, that's too much like hard labor."

"Well," said I, pausing to wipe the steam from my spectacles, "*this* isn't exactly a Book of Verses underneath the Bough."

At this moment the Amateur Skipper shot into the field of our vision, coming out of the yawl's depths like a jack-in-the-box.

"Cast off!" he yelled.

We were a few seconds late in grasping the fact that the Skipper had succeeded in starting the engine, and the *Cauliflower* just missed the dingey as she went by us. Fortunately, George had fastened the towline with one of the fancy knots that Bilger had taught him, a knot that came loose at the first yank. As it was, the line in snapping clear spun us sharply round.

The *Cauliflower* faded in the dusk.

"Now," said George, "if Bilger will only keep going and let us row home in peace—"

"He's coming back," said I.

"Can't stop the engine!" shouted the skipper, as he passed us; "afraid she won't start up again. But I'll pick you up." He began circling us, and in the fast-gathering darkness the yawl loomed as big and menacing as a battleship.

"Can you swim, Timby?" asked George resignedly.

"If I'm not crippled," said I.

"Then we'd better go overboard now. We don't really need Bilger's assistance."

"Look out!" called the Skipper. "I'm coming!"

The instinct of self-preservation led me to grasp the bobstay of the *Cauliflower* and swing clear of the dingey. I landed on the deck in an ungraceful sprawl, breathless.

"Isn't this exciting!" cried Miss Wilkins. Mrs. Bilger was kind enough to inquire whether I was hurt.

"Now for George!" said the Skipper, spinning the wheel to port.

"Never mind me!" shouted the artist, scarcely discernible in the gloom. "I'll row home. It's only eleven miles."

"Nonsense!" returned the Skipper, circling like a hawk. "Mind your eye, old man!"

"See here, Bilger," bawled the doomed and exasperated George; "I'm not a married man, but I have an aged mother dependent on me for support. I tell you, I don't want to be rescued. Keep off, or I'll sue you for damages."

The *Cauliflower* hit the dingey a glancing blow, and we had a glimpse of George clinging to the upturned gunwale.

"Now you *have* done it!" he yelled after us witheringly. "The oars are gone."

"Keep cool, old man!" rejoined Bilger. He drew another bead on the dingey. "Sweetheart, take the wheel."

"Yes, Lovest," said Mrs. Bilger tremulously, and the Skipper went forward.

He got George this time with a boat-hook. Then the inevitable happened: the engine, that had been working like a demon, suddenly quit.

Oh, no; not a bit of fiction inserted for dramatic effect; not at all. If you believe, as I do, that a malign spirit inhabits the shells of inanimate objects, you will understand that nothing could be more natural than that the engine should stop at that precise moment.

I pass over the next few hours. The plot petered out, the action dwindled to an irreducible minimum, and as my sentiments for Miss Wilkins never could be more than those of a friend, there was a total lack of heart-interest.

George, disgruntled, sat on the heel of the bowsprit and smoked pipe after pipe. Mrs. Bilger, Miss Wilkins, and I gathered in the cabin, where not a soul would care to sleep, and munched tea-biscuits, while the indefatigable Bilger sweated over the inert mechanism of the auxiliary, prattling cheerfully the while of batteries, spark-plugs, carbureters, and other foolish things.

Never have I known such exhaustless patience, such unfailing good-temper. He worked over that lifeless engine as one would over a drowned man. Now and then a spark of life leaped up; he fanned it tirelessly, and we made, perhaps, another mile. In this snail-like fashion we crawled to port.

"George," said the Skipper, "would you mind picking up the mooring?"

"Delighted," replied George morosely.

"Don't miss it," adjured Bilger, with the first touch of anxiety in his voice I had observed that day. "The tide is out, and we might hit the mud."

George got down on the bobstay, and peered low for a sight of the tin buoy. . . . We heard an ominous splash.

"I'm afraid George has fallen overboard," said Mrs. Bilger.

"How unfortunate!" said Miss Wilkins.

It was inevitable. I understood that perfectly; so did George. I leaned over the side and caught his upflung hand. He still had the boat-hook, hooked in the ring of the mooring.

Nothing of consequence was said. Words are symbols of ideas, but their emotional content is limited. Music would have better served, but there was no pianola aboard the *Cauliflower*.

We bundled silently into the dingey. Happily one oar remained, caught under a thwart; and George, to keep warm, paddled us up the river. If you have ever navigated a dingey containing five persons, you can guess within an hour or so, how long it takes to do a mile with one oar, counting zigzags. The clock in the steeple struck two when we made the landing.

"Thank you for a *very* interesting day," said Miss Wilkins to the Bilgers. I added my conventional appreciation.

"I wish," said the Amateur Skipper earnestly, "that you could get away for a cruise of four or five days. George and I have a trip all planned."

George and I walked homeward together.

"Where are you and Bilger going?" I inquired.

"I don't know where Bilger is going," replied George slowly, "and I don't know as I care a damn. But *I'm* going up in the Berkshires for the rest of the summer."

A CHANGE OF TREATMENT

BY W. W. JACOBS

A CHANGE OF TREATMENT

BY W. W. JACOBS

"YES, I've sailed under some 'cute skippers in my time," said the night-watchman; "them that go down in big ships see the wonders o' the deep, you know," he added with a sudden chuckle, "but the one I'm going to tell you about ought never to have been trusted out without 'is ma. A good many o' my skippers had fads, but this one was the worst I ever sailed under.

"It's some few years ago now; I'd shipped on his bark, the *John Elliott,* as slow-going an old tub as ever I was aboard of, when I was n't in quite a fit an' proper state to know what I was doing, an' I had n't been in her two days afore I found out his 'obby through overhearing a few remarks made by the second mate, who came up from dinner in a hurry to make 'em. 'I don't mind saws an' knives hung round the cabin,' he ses to the fust mate, 'but when a chap has a 'uman 'and alongside 'is plate, studying it while folks is at their food, it's more than a Christian man can stand.'

" 'That's nothing,' ses the fust mate, who had sailed with the bark afore. 'He's half crazy on doctoring. We nearly had a mutiny aboard once owing to his wanting to hold a *post mortem* on a man what fell from the mast-head. Wanted to see what the poor feller died of.'

"'I call it unwholesome,' ses the second mate very savage. 'He offered me a pill at breakfast the size of a small marble; quite put me off my feed, it did.'

"Of course, the skipper's fad soon got known for'-ard. But I didn't think much about it, till one day I seed old Dan'l Dennis sitting on a locker reading. Every now and then he'd shut the book, an' look up, closing 'is eyes, an' moving his lips like a hen drinking, an' then look down at the book again.

"'Why, Dan,' I ses, 'what's up? you ain't larning lessons at your time o' life?'

"'Yes, I am,' ses Dan very soft. 'You might hear me say it, it's this one about heart disease.'

"He hands over the book, which was stuck full o' all kinds o' diseases, and winks at me 'ard.

"'Picked it up on a book-stall,' he ses; then he shut 'is eyes an' said his piece wonderful. It made me quite queer to listen to 'im. 'That's how I feel,' ses he, when he'd finished. 'Just strength enough to get to bed. Lend a hand, Bill, an, go an' fetch the doctor.'

"Then I see his little game, but I wasn't going to run any risks, so I just mentioned, permiscous like, to the cook as old Dan seemed rather queer, an' went back an' tried to borrer the book, being always fond of reading. Old Dan pretended he was too ill to hear what I was saying, an' afore I could take it away from him, the skipper comes hurrying down with a bag in his 'and.

"'What's the matter, my man?' ses he, 'what's the matter?'

" 'I'm all right, sir,' ses old Dan, ' 'cept that I've been swoonding away a little.'

" 'Tell me exactly how you feel,' ses the skipper, feeling his pulse.

"Then old Dan said his piece over to him, an' the skipper shook his head an' looked very solemn.

" 'How long have you been like this?' he ses.

" 'Four or five years, sir,' ses Dan. 'It ain't nothing serious, sir, is it?'

" 'You lie quite still,' ses the skipper, putting a little trumpet thing to his chest an' then listening. 'Um! there's serious mischief here I'm afraid, the prognotice is very bad.'

" 'Prog what, sir?' ses Dan, staring.

" 'Prognotice,' ses the skipper, at least I think that's the word he said. 'You keep perfectly still, an' I'll go an' mix you up a draft, and tell the cook to get some strong beef-tea on.'

"Well, the skipper 'ad no sooner gone, than Cornish Harry, a great big lumbering chap o' six feet two, goes up to old Dan, an' he ses, 'Gimme that book.'

" 'Go away,' says Dan, 'don't come worrying 'ere; you 'eard the skipper say how bad my prognotice was.'

" 'You lend me the book,' ses Harry, ketching hold of him, 'or else I'll bang you first, and split to the skipper arterward. I believe I'm a bit consumptive. Anyway, I'm going to see.'

"He dragged the book away from the old man, and began to study. There was so many complaints in it he was almost tempted to have something else instead of consumption, but he decided on that at last, an' he got a cough what worried the foc'sle all night long, an' the next day, when the skipper came down to see Dan, he could 'ardly 'ear hisself speak.

" 'That's a nasty cough you've got, my man,' ses he, looking at Harry.

" 'Oh, it's nothing, sir,' ses Harry, careless like. 'I've 'ad it for months now off and on. I think it's perspiring so of a night does it.'

" 'What?' ses the skipper. 'Do you perspire of a night?'

" 'Dredful,' ses Harry. 'You could wring the clo'es out. I s'pose it's healthy for me, ain't it, sir?'

" 'Undo your shirt,' ses the skipper, going over to him, an' sticking the trumpet agin him. 'Now take a deep breath. Don't cough.'

" 'I can't help it, sir,' ses Harry, 'it will come. Seems to tear me to pieces.'

" 'You get to bed at once,' says the skipper, taking away the trumpet, an' shaking his 'ed. 'It's a fortunate thing for you, my lad, you're in skilled hands. With care, I believe I can pull you round. How does that medicine suit you, Dan?'

" 'Beautiful, sir,' says Dan. 'It's wonderful soothing, I slep' like a new-born babe arter it.'

" 'I'll send you to get some more,' ses the skipper. 'You're not to get up mind, either of you.'

" 'All right, sir,' ses the two in very faint voices, an' the skipper went away arter telling us to be careful not to make a noise.

"We all thought it a fine joke at first, but the airs them two chaps give themselves was something sickening. Being in bed all day, they was naturally wakeful of a night, and they used to call across the foc'sle inquiring arter each other's healths, an' waking us other chaps up. An' they 'ad swop beef-tea an' jellies with each other, an' Dan 'ud try an' coax a little port wine out o' Harry, which he 'ad to make blood with, but Harry 'ud say he hadn't made enough that day, an' he'd drink to the better health of old Dan's prognotice, an' smack his lips until it drove us a'most crazy to 'ear him.

"Arter these chaps had been ill two days, the other fellers began to put their heads together, being maddened by the smell o' beef-tea an' the like, an' said they was going to be ill too, and both the invalids got into a fearful state of excitement.

" 'You'll only spoil it for all of us,' ses Harry, 'and you don't know what to have without the book.'

" 'It's all very well doing your work as well as our own,' ses one of the men. 'It's our turn now. 'It's time you two got well.'

" '*Well?*' ses Harry, '*well?* Why you silly iggernerant chaps, we shan't never get well, people with our complaints never do. You ought to know that.'

" 'Well, I shall split,' ses one of them.

" 'You do!' ses Harry, 'you do, an' I'll put a 'ed on you that all the port wine and jellies in the world wouldn't cure. 'Sides, don't you think the skipper knows what's the matter with us?'

" 'Afore the other chaps could reply, the skipper hisself comes down, accompanied by the fust mate, with a look on his face which made Harry give the deepest and hollowest cough he'd ever done.

" 'What they reely want,' ses the skipper, turning to the mate, 'is keerful nussing.'

" 'I wish you'd let *me* nuss 'em,' ses the fust mate, 'only ten minutes—I'd put 'em both on their legs, an' running for their lives into the bargain, in ten minutes.'

" 'Hold your tongue, sir,' ses the skipper; 'what you say is unfeeling, besides being an insult to me. Do you think I studied medicine all these years without knowing when a man's ill?'

"The fust mate growled something, and went on deck, and the skipper started examining of 'em again. He said they was wonderfully patient lying in bed so long, an' he had 'em wrapped up in bed clo'es and carried on deck, so as the pure air could have a go at 'em.

"*We* had to do the carrying, an' there they sat, breathing the pure air, and looking at the fust mate out of the corners of their eyes. If they wanted anything from below one of us had to go an' fetch it, an' by the time they was taken down to bed again, we all resolved to be took ill too.

"Only two of 'em did it though, for Harry, who was a powerful, ugly-tempered chap, swore he'd do all sorts o' dreadful things to us if we didn't keep well and hearty, an' all 'cept these two did. One of 'em, Mike Rafferty, laid up with a swelling on his ribs, which I knew myself he 'ad 'ad for fifteen years, and the other chap had paralysis. I never saw a man so reely happy as the skipper was. He was up an' down with his medicines and his instruments all day long, and used to make notes of the cases in a big pocketbook, and read 'em to the second mate at meal-times.

"The foc'sle had been turned into hospital about a week, an' I was on deck doing some odd job or the other, when the cook comes up to me pulling a face as long as a fiddle.

" ' 'Nother invalid,' ses he; 'fust mate's gone stark, staring mad!'

" 'Mad?' ses I.

" 'Yes,' ses he. 'He's got a big basin in the galley, an' he's laughing like a hyener an' mixing bilge-water an' ink, an' paraffn an' butter an' soap an' all sorts o' things up together. The smell 's enough to kill a man; I've had to come away.'

"Curious-like, I jest walked up to the galley an' puts my 'ed in, an' there was the mate as the cook said, smiling all over his face, and ladling some thick sticky stuff into a stone bottle.

" 'How's the pore sufferers, sir?" ses he, stepping out of the galley jest as the skipper was going by.

" 'They're very bad; but I hope for the best,' ses the skipper, looking at him hard. 'I'm glad to see you're turned a bit more feeling.'

" 'Yes, sir,' ses the mate. 'I didn't think so at fust, but I can see now them chaps is all very ill. You'll s'cuse me saying it, but I don't quite approve of your treatment.'

"I thought the skipper would ha' bust.

" 'My treatment?' ses he. 'My treatment? What do you know about it?'

" 'You're treating 'em wrong, sir,' ses the mate. 'I have here' (patting the jar) 'a remedy which 'ud cure them all if you'd only let me try it.'

" 'Pooh!' ses the skipper. 'One medicine cure all diseases! The old story. What is it? Where'd you get it from?' ses he.

" 'I brought the ingredients aboard with me,' ses the mate. 'It's a wonderful medicine discovered by my grandmother, an' if I might only try it I'd thoroughly cure them pore chaps.'

"'Rubbish!' ses the skipper.

"'Very well, sir,' ses the mate, shrugging his shoulders. 'O' course, if you won't let me you won't. Still, I tell you, if you'd let me try I'd cure 'em all in two days. That's a fair challenge.'

"Well, they talked, and talked, and talked, until at last the skipper give way and went down below with the mate, and told the chaps they was to take the new medicine for two days, jest to prove the mate was wrong.

"'Let pore old Dan try it first, sir,' ses Harry, starting up, an' sniffing as the mate took the cork out; 'he's been awful bad since you've been away.'

"'Harry's worse than I am, sir,' ses Dan; 'it's only his kind heart that makes him say that.'

"'It don't matter which is fust,' ses the mate, filling a tablespoon with it, 'there's plenty for all. Now, Harry.'

"'Take it,' ses the skipper.

"Harry took it, an' the fuss he made you'd ha' thought he was swallering a football. It stuck all round his mouth, and he carried on so dredful that the other invalids was half sick afore it came to them.

"By the time the other three 'ad 'ad theirs it was as good as a pantermine, an' the mate corked the bottle up, and went an' sat down on a locker while they tried to rinse their mouths out with the luxuries which had been given 'em.

"'How do you feel?' ses the skipper.

"'I'm dying,' ses Dan.

" 'So'm I,' ses Harry; 'I b'leeve the mate's pisoned us.'

"The skipper looks over at the mate very stern an' shakes his 'ed slowly.

" 'It's all right,' ses the mate. 'It's always like that the first dozen or so doses.'

" 'Dozen or so doses!' ses old Dan, in a faraway voice.

" 'It has to be taken every twenty minutes,' ses the mate, pulling out his pipe and lighting it; an' the four men groaned all together.

" 'I can't allow it,' ses the skipper, 'I can't allow it. Men's lives mustn't be sacrificed for an experiment.'

" ''Tain't a experiment,' ses the mate very indignant, 'it's an old family medicine.'

" 'Well, they shan't have any more,' ses the skipper firmly.

" 'Look here,' ses the mate. 'If I kill any one o' these men, I'll give you twenty pound. Honor bright, I will.'

" 'Make it twenty-five,' ses the skipper, considering.

" 'Very good, ses the mate. 'Twenty-five; I can't say no fairer than that, can I? It's about time for another dose now.'

"He gave 'em another tablespoonful all round as the skipper left, an' the chaps what wasn't invalids nearly bust with joy. He wouldn't let 'em have anything to take the taste out, 'cos he said it didn't give the medicine a chance, an' he told us other chaps to remove the temptation, an' you bet we did.

"After the fifth dose, the invalids began to get desperate, an' when they heard they'd got to be woke up every twenty minutes through the night to take the stuff, they sort o' give up. Old Dan said he felt a gentle glow stealing over him and strengthening him, and Harry said that it felt like a healing balm to his lungs. All of 'em agreed it was a wonderful sort o' medicine, an' arter the sixth dose the man with paralysis dashed up on deck, and ran up the rigging like a cat. He sat there for hours spitting, an' swore he'd brain anybody who interrupted him, an' arter a little while Mike Rafferty went up and j'ined him, an' if the fust mate's ears didn't burn by reason of the things them two pore sufferers said about 'im, they ought to.

"They was all doing full work next day, an' though, o' course, the skipper saw how he'd been done, he didn't allude to it. Not in words, that is; but when a man tries to make four chaps do the work of eight, an' hits 'em when they don't, it's a easy job to see where the shoe pinches."

A PLEASANT NIGHT IN SPRING

BY STEPHEN FRENCH WHITMAN

A PLEASANT NIGHT IN SPRING

BY STEPHEN FRENCH WHITMAN

TWO young men were watching from an open window of a town club-house, the end of a beautiful spring afternoon. The avenue without, beneath a sky all delicately yellow, was full of an amber-colored radiance, curiously thick, through which, shining as though powdered daintily with gold, moved traffic of the finer, ornamental sorts. The happy listlessness of spring was in the outside air; it impelled passing gentlemen to wear, above their cool-hued, summery garments, expressions gently pleased, perhaps in some cases tender, or even, it may be, romantic; it impelled passing ladies to display, along with flowery hats and filmy gowns, excessive, unnecessary, almost reprehensible attractiveness. Inside, to these two young men, the listlessness of spring had evidently found its way, but not so, apparently, had the happiness. With round, sad eyes, dejected mouths, and tucked-in chins they sat, each low in his deep chair, surveying, between little sips from cocktail glasses, the beauty of the evening misanthropically.

Presently, said one of these young men—the short, stout one—looking out over the amber-tinted avenue with a face full of weary cynicism:

"Gwynnie, by what deplorable accident were you

and I born so many centuries too late? Here is spring stirring when, in other, happier times, brave knights were irresistibly tempted to fare forth in search of strange adventure. Imagine me, Gwynnie, in my proper setting, beautifully polished cap-à-pie, brave horse underneath, sword at thigh, mouthful of vernal couplets, heart hot with the desire for wonderful encounters. Hist, says I, drawing rein under the leaves. Little screams in the heart of the woods; a lady in distress; scaly dragons to slay; low-browed tyrants to hoist on a spear point. A clatter of steel, a bellow, a snatch of song, a kiss! Alas, I should have been a knight.

"Look out, now, on this pretty street. It shines bewitchingly from a spring sunset. Its air seems enriched with little golden particles. Its very breeze is mildly intoxicating, unless I am mistaken. There, you would venture, lies a region of sweet promise. But, believe me, Gwynnie, its allure is false. Its giltish look is a veneer, covering and disguising the commonplace. Its breeze just for the moment deceptively perfumes stale monotony. If you and I were tempted by it this evening, if we went out, answering its false seduction, yearning and hoping for adventure, what should we gain at best? Nothing but the obvious and the everyday. The world to-night is a dreadful, common place made up of stuffy theater seats, the odorous insides of hansom cabs, restaurant tablecloths with an ineradicable fruit-stain on each one, and salons full of frail French furniture with knock-kneed legs. Of such things, Gwynnie, must any evening entertainment that we undertake be full. Seriously, I assure you that the world is Bowdlerized. Romance is dead. There is no such thing, to-day, as real adventure. And this evening, how passionately something in me longs for real adventure!"

The young man sighed heavily and, with a practised finger, tapped a bell on a little table. A servant appearing almost instantly, the young man said sadly, for the tenth time that afternoon:

"Take Mr. Pengwynne's order."

Over the avenue settled slowly a golden hint of dusk; failing sunshine was mixed there with a little mist. Through that nebulous atmosphere, street lamps, too early lighted, glowed faintly, disseminating the most pallid shades of lavender. A passing carriage, now and then, showed kindled lamps. Up to the carved cornices of the houses went flying, one by one, the sparrows, to meet in twittering, ruffling groups upon the thresholds of their night's lodgings.

Mr. Pengwynne—he who was tall and thin—sedately took up the conversation:

"Tubby," said he, "I am not pleased with you this evening. Young, healthy, excessively well nourished, overprosperous, here you lie back, with your waistcoat contumeliously in the air, sneering at the world to-day. Adventure! Where is not adventure in this strange city full of everything, in this teeming, mysterious isle?"

"Oh, pooh!" retorted Mr. Tuebal pettishly. "Adventure there may be, of a sort to tickle little minds: cheap stuff, ordinary, unoriginal stuff. Real romance, I repeat—romance fit for great souls—is dead." So saying, he hurled himself farther down in his deep chair, in an attitude of utter despondency.

"Well," remarked Mr. Pengwynne calmly, "I disagree with you. You may be pleased to learn that I, too, by this time, feel somewhat knight-errantish; but I shall not lie here and let that feeling torture me. *'Res, non verbæ,'* is the motto of my family, which you may read on my ring, if you have any doubts. I am for adventure, and I invite you to share it."

"It will be poor," said Mr. Tuebal grudgingly. "Be warned beforehand, nothing new will come of it. The world is Bowdlerized."

They left the club-house and moved sedately down the avenue. The last of the sunlight, as though it had lingered overtime just for this opportunity, illumined them with a vague refulgence—an office almost unnecessary as the painting of the lily. No lady but would have observed them anyway with pretty, askance interest; no gentleman but would have noticed their subtly harmonious attire with approbation and respect. The sunshine at last reluctantly withdrew. Walking on, through a dusk pierced capriciously with countless foggy lights, Mr. Pengwynne and Mr. Tuebal gazed always mystically ahead, as though watching for the first far-off looming of adventure.

Chance, turning them presently from the avenue and into a side street, brought them before a little church. This structure nestled so modestly behind a fat, ecclesiastical sort of hedge that only its squat roof was visible from the sidewalk—unless one stopped, as Mr. Pengwynne and Mr. Tuebal did involuntarily, directly before the gateway. From that point one might see within a low stone doorway, and at this evening hour, on either side of it a rich, soft glimmer of multi-colored light shining through stained-glass windows. The two young men, moved to admiration by this unusual vista, stood discussing seriously its inappropriateness in the city. They observed, with half-closed eyes and tilted heads, its truly bucolic quality.

"The Church of Our Lady of Rocamadour," read Mr. Pengwynne, from a little sign beside the gate. "Oh, yes," he remembered, "where the runaways get married. How pleasant, if there could be a wedding while we wait!"

"Little good that would do us," said Mr. Tuebal sourly.

"Little harm, too, Tubby, you may thank your stars. Observe, now; there is an empty hansom cab waiting yonder; the church is illuminated; evidently some one is inside. Who knows what interesting romance may not be at its crisis here?"

"Does that concern us?" asked Mr. Tuebal, leaning apathetically against his friend.

"Everything," declared Mr. Pengwynne, "concerns your genuine adventurer."

Mr. Tuebal, drawn along by the arm, but hanging back, mumbled that this was ridiculous.

"Not yet; but I will not deny that it may contain ridiculous possibilities," responded Mr. Pengwynne, and dragged him through the doorway.

The little church, a cozy place, was dimly lighted. In the chancel were five persons; a charitably smiling old minister in vestments, a lean and gloomy sexton, a stout, abashed hansom cabman, an elderly gentleman in a tight frock coat, and a beautiful young woman wonderfully attired in raiment over which was written, for Mr. Pengwynne and Mr. Tuebal to read with their discerning, worldly eyes: "Made in Paris and paid for with a sigh." This group was so arranged that no one with sense could have doubted what it was engaged in.

Mr. Pengwynne and Mr. Tuebal, arm in arm, leaning gracefully on each other, observed the scene respectfully. But finally, not very respectfully, commented Mr. Pengwynne:

"May and December. She marries him, but why? Inspect him, Tubby; this dim religious light is kind to him, but one may see a part. Note his excessive, general uncomeliness; his shameless, glistening dome, his fishy eyes, his purple chops, his baggy-kneed, decrepit pose! Is this pretty lady blind? Faugh! I am horrified!"

"He looks like money," said Mr. Tuebal, cynically.

"You have reason, Tubby," assented Mr. Pengywnne, staring coldly at the bridegroom. "Now do you see what pitiable ailment this pretty lady has? Alas, you and I are witnesses of a dreadful, antique crime to-night. The present slips away, the past surrounds us. There, before you, rears the villainous, scaly dragon—knight errantry, its enemy—about to pounce upon the helpless maiden! Does she cry out? No. Why not? Why, there she cowers charmed into helplessness—for in each eyeball of yonder diabolical creature shines banefully the image of a little dollar-mark!"

Mr. Tuebal regarded Mr. Pengwynne with a startled gaze.

"Why, then, the lady being helpless and we knights errant for the evening, why do we stand here idle?" he asked anxiously.

"We do not, Tubby," Mr. Pengwynne assured him, and added ominously:

"Follow me."

Mr. Pengwynne stalked slowly forward, one hand thrust into the bosom of his waistcoat, his hat held out before him, top up, across his free arm. He carried himself, in fact, just in that neat, formal attitude which was the chosen pose of all great men before the camera, in those days when Daguerre took the pictures. Mr. Tuebal, aptly taking the hint, followed in another attitude, no less imposing of its sort. Some famous tragedy actor must have served him as his model. He dragged his feet, seeing to it that one was always far behind; between every two steps he doddered slightly.

It was just at this moment that the minister reached that point in the marriage service where one is requested, if he knows any good reason for prohibition of the ceremony, to speak forthwith, or else forever hold his peace. The good old man, having mumbled this request without the slightest display of anxiety, was on the point of finishing his work, when—

"This marriage must not be," announced Mr. Pengwynne, in serious, calm tones, coming to a stop before the chancel steps.

The five participants, whirling around as one, gaped at the two intruders. The cabman swallowed something suddenly and then looked sick; the sexton's gloomy countenance was lighted with a flash of genuine interest; the minister appeared to doubt his ears; the lady trembled so that all her Paris plumes were agitated; the bridegroom's red face swelled alarmingly, like those balloons which little boys burst, sometimes, in blowing up. It was the bridegroom who finally broke the silence, with a sort of muffled roar.

"Ha! Harumph! Am I in my senses? Who the

dickens are you, sir? And what do you mean, sir, by this villainous impertinence?"

Mr. Pengwynne, gracefully raising a well-kept forefinger, waggled it admonishingly. When he replied it was with the slightest foreign accent. Said he:

"You, sir, do not need to ask me what I mean, if you take honest counsel with your conscience. I shall be sorry if you force me to be more explicit in this gathering."

"By George, sir," ejaculated the bridegroom, between two snorts, with a wild gesticulation, "you had better be explicit!"

"Very well, then," said Mr. Pengwynne coldly, his foreign accent becoming more pronounced. "Allow me to inform you, though I think superfluously, that a certain lady in waiting to her Highness, the Princess of the Asturias—ees—not—daid!"

Mr. Tuebal started, flashed a sidelong glance of admiration at his friend, and slid swiftly into a distinctly Latin pose. As for the bridegroom, he stood as though frozen midway between two intelligible gestures, in the most unique attitude imaginable.

"Princess of the Asturias!" he gasped. "Lady in waiting! What— What, Heaven save us, what have we here!"

"Her representatives, my dear sir," replied Mr. Pengwynne, designating himself and his companion with a courtly gesture. "Or rather, the representatives of her mistress's royal brother, his Catholic Majesty, Alfonso, who will not see unmoved, believe me, any injury to one of the most beauteeful and gentille ladies of hees realm."

"Why—" The bridegroom, wheezing impotently at Mr. Pengwynne and Tuebal, finally achieved:

"Why—this is monstrous! I was never in my life in Spain!"

"I did not say so," said Mr. Pengwynne. "Perhaps, though, you may have been in Paris?"

"Ha! And what has that to do with it?" gurgled the bridegroom, trying to stretch his collar.

"Señor," said Mr. Pengwynne, turning confidently to Mr. Tuebal, "produce, if you please, the papers; the record of the marriage, both civil and religious, in the twenty-fifth arrondissement of Paris, the copy of the inscription relative to that marriage in the archives of the Espanish nobility, and the three hundred and twenty-one love letters of this gentleman, together with his written desires regarding the education of his little heirs."

"Señor," answered Mr. Tuebal quite as confidently, after a moment of deep thought, "zat can not be done. Zey are not wiz me."

"Not wiz you!" cried Mr. Pengwynne anxiously.

"Ah, no. Behol'! Zis morning, when you to me zem give, I send zem at once to our Ambassador at Washington, along wiz all ze claims of abandon, so he may have zem at hand when he ze disposition of zis case displays before ze Presidente. But if zis bigammie is commit, we can require zem again pronto—most quick, for—what you say—ze extradeesion of zis señor?"

"Ah!" exclaimed Mr. Pengwynne regretfully. "Then I can do nothing more at present, and must beg leave to retire as I have come, leaving onlee my protest. I regret, señorita. Adios, señor. We shall meet again."

Turning, rearranging his hat across his arm, thrusting a hand into the bosom of his waistcoat, Mr. Pengwynne withdrew in stately fashion. Mr. Tuebal, following, bore himself less tragically than at his entrance; adaptability was his forte; his exit was in the jaunty and yet haughty manner of your true hidalgo of Castile. Gaining the door and passing through it, they left behind them a group as motionless and rigid as those which in museums of waxworks portray episodes almost as tremendous.

Mr. Pengwynne and Mr. Tuebal, once out-of-doors, crossed the street with alacrity. Ascending a brown-stone stoop, they perched themselves comfortably at its top, in the deep shadow of the doorway. They sniffed with relish the fresh, cool evening air, faintly perfumed, with just the barest hint in it of dewy trees and grasses—an odor borne to those stone wastes of the city almost miraculously, one would say, from who knows how distant a sweet sylvan spot. This far-fetched scent of budding spring affected Mr. Tuebal like a charm. It conjured up in him emotions tenderly romantic. Dreamily he asked:

"Gwynnie, will she marry him?"

"How can she?" said Mr. Pengwynne, admiring the spangled sky. "How can she when he is already married to a lady in waiting of the Princess of the Asturias, whose proofs of abandon are in the hands of the Espanish ambassador at Washington? Be at ease, Tubby, she will not marry him."

"Look, look!" whispered Mr. Tuebal. "Some one is coming out."

Through the low stone doorway opposite burst in evident agitation the lady, the bridegroom and the hansom cabman. They rushed across the sidewalk. The cabman scrambled up on his hansom cab. The lady sprang inside. The bridegroom seemed to be boggling ineffectively before the cab-doors. The cabman lashed his horse; the cab-doors were slammed shut; the vehicle, careening recklessly in a wide circle, made for the avenue. Alone upon the sidewalk, the bridegroom stood and watched it disappear. Then, suddenly waving his fists toward the housetops in a strange, extravagant gesture, he went, hopping and stamping, off the other way. The shadows swallowed his eccentric figure. The soft light in the stained-glass windows of the little church popped out abruptly. Silence prevailed. The street was as lonely and as tranquil as a country lane.

"The maiden saved, exit the dragon, cheated of his prey. What more is left for us, Tubby, to desire?"

"Several things for me. Lights and soft music, with plenty of flute-notes scattered through the score. Lights and little square tables; tinkling fountains and attentive waiters. Happiness always gives me an appetite. I am for dinner beginning with opalescent cocktails and ending with the largest, most unctuous cigars."

"Your soul is in your stomach, Tubby," said Mr. Pengwynne with a sigh. "I, for my part, could feed just upon this lovely evening."

"Not so here. French knickknacks for this señor," quoth Mr. Tuebal with a smack. "Gimcracks of cookery—everything the doctor tells one not to touch

—and something twinkling in a glass, replenished every time one looks away. Come, come, you have got me thinking about food; quick, to the restaurant—this is torture!"

"Well, well," said Mr. Pengwynne indulgently, after a last lingering gaze aloft. With infinite solicitude each helped the other down the steps. Arm in arm, they set out.

II

A WAITER had poured out for Mr. Pengwynne and Mr. Tuebal two little cupfuls of coffee. A fatherly headwaiter had brought a case of fat cigars, and two of these—each about a foot long, rich chocolate-colored, their coats of texture like the finest velvet—ornamented the engaging faces of these two young men. Leaning back in their comfortable chairs, both listened with closed eyes to music coming mysteriously from some screened orchestra—music which, as Mr. Tuebal had desired, had many little, soft falls, tremblings and twitterings of flute-notes. One might almost have thought that these two young men, lulled by melody, had fallen sound asleep. But, finally, Mr. Tuebal, half raising one eyelid, inquired: "Gwynnie, now what are you thinking of?"

"You will be surprised," responded Mr. Pengwynne, after some introspection. "I have remorseful thoughts."

"Remorseful!"

"Yes. Regarding our knight-errantry."

"You regret it!"

"Well, partly. On this account: we have done a

pretty lady a great favor, and I am glad of that. We have confounded the dragon, and I find nothing to regret in that. But, Tubby, there remains the minister. We have done him an injury."

"How so?" inquired Mr. Tuebal, opening both eyes.

"We have deprived him of his wedding fee."

"Why! So we have!" cried Mr. Tuebal in astonishment.

"That is a little church, Tubby, and, I suspect, not a rich one. The minister of a little church is not a millionaire. I imagine that few luxuries surround him. He inhabits no hansom cabs. He drinks no vintage wines. Mushrooms sous cloche are strangers to his palate. His treasures are nearly all laid up in heaven. But one must live while here, and wedding fees undoubtedly help one to do so. We have done wrong, Tubby, and it is for that reason that I am remorseful."

"And so am I. I am ashamed of both of us," said Mr. Tuebal—and, after a moment's thought, with an expression of bright intelligence, exclaimed:

"We must make restitution!"

"Undoubtedly that is what we should do. But how?"

Mr. Pengwynne, smoking violently, frowning at the gilded ceiling, considered, while Mr. Tuebal waited with a hopeful face exquisitely attentive. Suddenly Mr. Pengwynne's anxiety gave place to relief. He smiled at Mr. Tuebal reassuringly.

"All is well, Tubby," said he. "I know what we shall do. We shall bring him another couple and let him marry them."

Mr. Tuebal rose half out of his chair, ejaculating: "Another couple!"

"Why not?" said Mr. Pengwynne. "Have we not just broken up a marriage? There we accomplished the greater labor; beside that one this other will be child's play. For surely it is much simpler to make a marriage than to break one! That is a well-worn axiom; it descends to us from very ancient times; I suspect that it was a byword even among the loutish suitors of Penelope."

Mr. Pengwynne—while Mr. Tuebal watched him as though dizzy with delight—turned with deliberation and surveyed calculatingly the surrounding diners.

The room was crowded to its utmost. The music finished, above innumerable sleekly brushed heads and elaborately fluted coiffures, rose an intermittent, sealike murmur as wave after wave of talk rose rapidly out of monotone and broke with little splashes of light laughter. A gentle breeze from the open windows wandered throughout the room, setting to nodding the flowers on the tables, sending cigar-smoke curling fantastically in wide, gray ribbons overhead, carrying everywhere a strange, sweet scent, quite distinguishable from the odors of tobacco and of coffee, peculiarly seductive: the subtle mixture of half a hundred different perfumes.

"That lady all in mauve-colored things," said Mr. Pengwynne, after sniffing carefully several times, "wears chypre. I am notoriously for any one who wears chypre, Tubby, and I feel very kindly toward this lady for that reason. Why should we not help her to get married this evening?

"See, it is most auspicious—there is no doubt about her young man. Observe that she attracts him. He lops over the table at her; he looks as though, if he but dared, he would just as lief as not take her at a bite. She, leaning back, is coy and anxious; she looks about her stealthily to see if she is perceived by any one she knows. I think she is accustomed to a chaperon at dinner. She is convinced that she is doing something very sporting this evening. A pleasant, modest girl! Well, shall we, speaking vulgarly, splice them up?"

"She will want a large wedding," asserted Mr. Tuebal pessimistically. "I know the kind. A dozen bridesmaids, a maid of honor, and, ahead, a couple of little curly-headed girls with skinny white silk legs, scattering flowers. No elopements for that sort, but pageantry. Besides, her young man, while he is all well enough, looks pathetically conventional. His mind moves slavishly by rule. The bizarre would jar him. Even our little proposition would jar him."

"We shall see," said Mr. Pengwynne. "Come, let us be at it. Wait, we must pay this. Heads or tails?" "Tails," cried Mr. Tuebal inadvisedly, and paid the bill.

The two young men arose and, Mr. Pengwynne leading, strolled toward their prey. What sort of talk was she listening to then, wide-eyed and intent—that chypre-scented lady all in mauve-colored things? Could it be the sentimental prelude to a real proposal, which would smooth the way remarkably for Messrs. Pengwynne and Tuebal? Far from it, worse luck; for, as the conspirators drew close, that fatuous young man was only telling her:

"Next day we took the train from Moscow and went straight to Berlin, and that was why I missed your letter."

"Moscow!" said Mr. Pengwynne below his breath, turning and lifting an eyebrow significantly at Mr. Tuebal. Inspiration flashed in his eyes. Gracefully stepping forward, bending over the maiden, cocking his head severely toward her escort, he asked her confidentially:

"Pardon me, but is this gentleman annoying you?"

The escort sat dumfounded for a moment—then got up on his feet. "Sir!" he uttered incredulously.

"And sir to you," said Mr. Pengwynne icily, for his part.

The strange young man turned bright red as far as could be seen. All in a twitter, he blurted out:

"Will you step outside with me a moment?"

"Percival!" pathetically cried out the lady, clasping her hands.

Mr. Pengwynne, with a low bow to her, said to her escort: "I shall await you in the lobby," and, with Mr. Tuebal, grandly stalked off thither.

Almost immediately, in the lobby, behold the strange young man hurling himself on the scene, breathing hard through his nose.

"Now, sir!" he exclaimed, closely approaching Mr. Pengwynne. "An explanation!"

"My dear young friend," said Mr. Pengwynne, smiling at him sadly and with that unexpected smile utterly confounding him, "forgive this unconventional means of drawing you out here. It was the only one which happened just now to occur to me. Perhaps it was a trifle extravagant—"

"Extravagant!" the young man gasped. Mr. Tuebal solicitously offered him an arm.

"But you will forgive me when you hear my news," continued Mr. Pengwynne. "Sir, my dear young friend, if I may call you so, she is in New York!"

The young man's chin hung down.

"She is in New York!" he repeated idiotically.

"The Russian," added Mr. Pengwynne profoundly. "She is hunting for you."

The young man gazed all about him helplessly. Suddenly a look of concrete horror filled his face. His gaze was jerked back at Mr. Pengwynne.

"Not—" he whispered wildly—"not the Countess?"

"The Countess," immediately assented Mr. Pengwynne, with a sigh of relief.

Dashing a hand across his forehead, the young man chattered:

"But this is absurd! I had nothing to do with her. I merely saw her in Petersburg and again in Moscow. Three mornings in succession, in the hotel in Moscow, she sent boutonnières to my table. Once only I met her where I could not get away: in the lift. She thought the lift was going to drop. She clung to me, and—I found a ruby ring in my pocket afterward—which I returned by post," the young man ended miserably with a blush.

"Ah, me," said Mr. Pengwynne, nodding at Mr. Tuebal. "You see? A Russian custom. She thinks now she is engaged to him. At any rate, sir, here she is, and swears to marry you. She would have had me for her lawyer, but when I saw you to-night your youth, your happiness, your devotion elsewhere, I had the heart no more. I am for you, now, to the bitter end. My dear young friend, give me your hand!"

"She swears to marry me!" repeated the young man in hollow tones, allowing his limp hand to be pumped up and down violently by Mr. Pengwynne.

"Willy-nilly, in fact. Marriage, or else a frightful row. Ah, you, at least, know what these Russians are! Assuredly, she will do it, unless—"

Mr. Pengwynne came closer. He whispered in the young man's ear:

"There is one way by which you might escape. Suppose that you were already married?"

"Well?"

"Why, why, wake up! Then she would be foiled!"

"But," babbled the young man wildly, "I am not married. And I do not want to marry her. Deuce take it all, I want to marry some one else!"

"Aha!" gurgled Mr. Pengwynne, slapping him on the back with frightful jocularity. "You do, eh, you gay dog? Why, be about it, then!" He waved his hand in a florid and suggestive gesture toward the dinner room. "Marry her to-night, Percival," said he, "and you are saved!"

The young man sat him down limply on the edge of a fern pot.

"My head reels," he confessed feebly. "I—I can not do anything like that. No notice! Nothing in order! It is so—irregular." Mr. Tuebal snorted.

"She would never consent," the young man added as an afterthought.

"But you, I take it," suggested Mr. Pengwynne, "could stand the irregularities if she would consent? I think so, rather—and especially, if you had seen your

Countess this afternoon sweeping her glittering train up and down my private office, gritting her little teeth, scattering tears, La Ferme cigarette smoke and Frenchy scents!"

The young man shuddered and wrung his hands protesting: "This is some ghastly dream!"

"Look, now," said Mr. Pengwynne, suddenly becoming masterful. "I am your friend, am I not? Leave this to me. I shall persuade the lady yonder."

"You?"

"Give me five minutes with her and you shall see. Is it a bargain? Say nothing—I know instinctively it is. Wait here, then. Expect me in five minutes, with the lady!"

In another moment Mr. Pengwynne was sitting opposite the lady whom they had left in the dinner room. She, probably never so aghast before in all her life, stared wildly at her *vis-à-vis,* toward the empty doorway and back again. Her charming little chin began to quiver, and Mr. Pengwynne remorsefully made haste to reassure her.

"Dear lady," suavely said he, "be tranquil. All is well. Percival is in the hall, intact. And you may rest assured for a moment here with me, for I am his most valuable friend, and there is something of the greatest moment which I must disclose to you. Bear with me—I shall be as brief as possible."

Leaning over the table, Mr. Pengwynne impressively began:

"When Percival was recently in Russia a wild adventure caught him in its toils, with the most extraordinary consequences.

"One night while wandering in Moscow through

the meaner streets he was accosted by a ragged stranger, who asked him where he came from. 'America,' Percival answered proudly, and added, perhaps imprudently, but with the best of intentions, 'the home of freedom.' 'Good,' said the stranger. 'Come with me,' and, linking arms with Percival, hurried him off, up and down alleys and finally through the portals of an ill-favored, gloomy house. There, pressing upon a secret panel, he ushered Percival into a bright room full of determined-looking men. 'Here,' said the ragged stranger, removing his false beard, 'is our new brother from America.'

"Up rose that assembly as one man. But, 'Ah!' cried one harsh voice, 'here is some fatal mistake! This person is not the one! We are betrayed!' Drawing a hundred various weapons, they rushed at Percival, and I assure you that in another moment they would have finished him had not his conductor thrown himself before our young friend's body. 'Hold!' bellowed he imperatively. 'Do nothing until I question him. Have you forgotten that we kill only when it is necessary?'

"This gave them pause. Surrounding poor Percival like so many wolves, they plied him with violent inquiries. He, brave—as you may imagine—even in that situation, answered all candidly until they were forced to admit that he was innocent of any wrong intentions. To make a long story short, they decided not to kill him then and there, but all declared that he must take their awful oath of secrecy and loyalty. Behold our Percival, dear lady, to save his life compelled to swear allegiance to the Nihilists!

"Well, I shall make haste for your sake. That very

night, and in that room, they drew lots to see who should assassinate the Czar. And Percival, forced to draw, like the rest, his slip out of a muzhik's greasy cap, found that, through some horrible caprice of chance, he held the fatal ballot!

"I shall pass over all his mental agony at that moment, and when later, with diabolical ingenuity, his grisly companions explained to him what he should do. All was arranged for two days later, when he was to go to Peterhof with a bomb concealed beneath his derby hat. But the next day, evading somehow with the ingeniousness of desperation the Nihilist spies who dogged his footsteps, he managed to escape from Moscow to Berlin!

"But now, observe. To those implacable Nihilists he is a traitor who holds all their lives in his hand. In their opinion he merits a hideous death. So everywhere he has gone their executioners have gone speeding after him like bloodhounds on a scent. At last they have reached New York. At last they have discovered his exact whereabouts. In fact, when I looked out just now into the street there was one leaning against the lamppost, picking his teeth with disgusting cynicism and hiding under his arm a little package whose contents I can guess at with a shudder. Ah, dear lady, Nemesis is waiting there on the corner of the avenue! Heaven help us! Is this not a serious enough affair?"

Mr. Pengwynne concluding, the lady sat there motionless from horror. Finally she was able to utter:

"Merciful gracious! What is to be done?"

"Listen," said Mr. Pengwynne, springing nimbly to

that cue. "There is just one way by which Percival can be saved. He must be married instantly."

"Married!" she blurted out.

"And instantly. The only virtue of these wretches is a certain rude sort of chivalry. They will not harm a lady. And if Percival for a few days could be accompanied constantly by some fair companion, so that they could not harm him without risk of harming her, they would be foiled. For in a few days I shall have found means to circumvent them. But to-night we are in the most intense danger. Yes, there is but one hope. He must be married instantly."

"But—" tremulously she began.

"Come," said Mr. Pengwynne pathetically. "Will you not toss a few scruples to the winds and marry Percival to save him?"

"Why—why—" the lady faltered. "He has not asked me."

"I ask you," exclaimed Mr. Pengwynne. "I, his ambassador, beseech you. Aside from this affair you are his only thought by day, his single dream by night. He sees you in the clouds, the sunset, the flowers, the rising moon. He peaks and pines for you. Dear lady, he adores you. Marry and save him. Take into sanctuary that doting heart. And quick! That dreadful emissary may tire of waiting and wander into the lobby."

"Let us go to him," cried she, and Mr. Pengwynne, ignoring the general interest and admiration of the diners, in courtly fashion guided her trembling feet toward the hall.

There her young man rushed forward from among the fern pots.

"Geraldine!" he stammered, almost misdoubting, evidently, that misty, incoherent smile she squandered on him.

"Percival!" she gasped. "My hero!"

"You know?"

"All."

"And—and—and—"

"Incredible dummy!" fumed Mr. Tuebal, ready to dance with impatience.

"—and yet—you love me?" the young man managed to get out.

"Percy!" she breathed, looking for some arms to sink into and finding, after a little waiting, Percival's.

"Tubby," requested Mr. Pengwynne softly, serenely, competently—the admirable Pengwynne through and through—"a four-wheeler, for the Church of Our Lady of Rocamadour."

They saw them well married, did Messrs. Pengwynne and Tuebal, in the little chancel where the musty, stale, sweet odor of extinct incense mingled with the worldly aroma of chypre. The sexton had gone home and the good old minister—it turned out fortunately for those two young men—was as nearsighted as he was benevolent. Geraldine and Percival he made one with Mr. Tuebal's fat signet ring; for Mr. Tuebal was the groomsman, while Mr. Pengwynne, responding in a feeble and shaky voice appropriate in one well along in years, with a sort of antiquated grace gave away the bride. At last they packed the bridal pair into the four-wheeler. Two faces looked out through the window—two faces strangely dazed, incredulous and awed.

"Where to?" the cabman asked.

"To the Elysian rose-gardens," promptly directed Mr. Pengwynne. "To the end of the rainbow. To Arcadia. To the undiscovered country behind the moon. Off with you, cabby; your horse is taking cold."

"The devil!" vouchsafed the cabman in bewilderment, and drove furiously away.

Mr. Pengwynne and Mr. Tuebal, alone together in the dark street, followed the progress of the four-wheeler with keen attention. Presently, when there was left of it just a little rocking shadow far away, Mr. Tuebal began to sing tenderly in a sweet tenor:

> "*And all the sky was powdered bright*
> *With stars that shed their heav'nly light*
> *On Damon neat and Chloe sweet,*
> *Whilst rode those two away, away,*
> *A fine new world to see!*
> *Oh, Hymen, Hymenee!*"

And Mr. Pengwynne, joining him with a rich and throaty barytone, they marched off, passionately caroling in unison:

> "*And there were chubby cupids limned*
> *Upon the coach-door cunningly;*
> *The very sylvan birdies hymned:*
> *Oh, Hymen, Hymenee!*
> *Oh, Hymen, Hymenee!*"

Mr. Tuebal, his head thrown back in abandon, suddenly stopped short and grasped his companion's arm.

"Oh, Gwynnie!" he cried, choking with esthetic joy. "Look! 'Over the roofs the honey-colored moon!'"

Stock-still, legs spread out like sailors on a heaving deck, for minute after minute they gazed in silence, with rapt faces, up into the radiant night.

THE COUNT AND THE WEDDING GUEST

BY O. HENRY

THE COUNT AND THE WEDDING GUEST

BY O. HENRY

ONE evening when Andy Donovan went to dinner at his Second Avenue boarding-house, Mrs. Scott introduced him to a new boarder, a young lady, Miss Conway. Miss Conway was small and unobtrusive. She wore a plain, snuffy-brown dress, and bestowed her interest, which seemed languid, upon her plate. She lifted her diffident eyelids and shot one perspicuous, judicial glance at Mr. Donovan, politely murmured his name, and returned to her mutton. Mr. Donovan bowed with the grace and beaming smile that were rapidly winning for him social, business and political advancement, and erased the snuffy-brown one from the tablets of his consideration.

Two weeks later Andy was sitting on the front steps enjoying his cigar. There was a soft rustle behind and above him, and Andy turned his head—and had his head turned.

Just coming out the door was Miss Conway. She wore a night-black dress of *crêpe de—crêpe de*—oh, this thin black goods. Her hat was black, and from it drooped and fluttered an ebon veil, filmy as a spider's web. She stood on the top step and drew on black silk gloves. Not a speck of white or a spot of color about her dress anywhere. Her rich golden hair was drawn, with scarcely a ripple, into a shining, smooth knot low on her neck. Her face was plain rather than pretty, but it was now illuminated and made almost beautiful by her large gray eyes that gazed above the houses across the street into the sky with an expression of the most appealing sadness and melancholy.

Gather the idea, girls—all black, you know, with the preference for *crêpe de*—oh, *crêpe de Chine*—that's it. All black, and that sad, faraway look, and the hair shining under the black veil (you have to be a blonde, of course), and try to look as if, although your young life had been blighted just as it was about to give a hop-skip-and-a-jump over the threshold of life, a walk in the park might do you good, and be sure to happen out the door at the right moment, and —oh, it'll fetch 'em every time. But it's fierce, now, how cynical I am, ain't it?—to talk about mourning costumes this way.

Mr. Donovan suddenly reinscribed Miss Conway upon the tablets of his consideration. He threw away the remaining inch-and-a-quarter of his cigar, that would have been good for eight minutes yet, and quickly shifted his center of gravity to his low-cut patent leathers.

"It's a fine, clear evening, Miss Conway," he said; and if the Weather Bureau could have heard the confident emphasis of his tones it would have hoisted the square white signal and nailed it to the mast.

"To them that has the heart to enjoy it, it is, Mr. Donovan," said Miss Conway, with a sigh.

Mr. Donovan in his heart cursed fair weather.

Heartless weather! It should hail and blow and snow to be consonant with the mood of Miss Conway.

"I hope none of your relatives—I hope you haven't sustained a loss?" ventured Mr. Donovan.

"Death has claimed," said Miss Conway, hesitating —"not a relative, but one who—but I will not intrude my grief upon you, Mr. Donovan."

"Intrude?" protested Mr. Donovan. "Why, say, Miss Conway, I'd be delighted, that is, I'd be sorry —I mean I'm sure nobody could sympathize with you truer than I would."

Miss Conway smiled a little smile. And oh, it was sadder than her expression in repose.

" 'Laugh, and the world laughs with you; weep, and they give you the laugh,' " she quoted.

"I have learned that, Mr. Donovan. I have no friends or acquaintances in this city. But you have been kind to me. I appreciate it highly."

He had passed her the pepper twice at the table.

"It's tough to be alone in New York—that's a cinch," said Mr. Donovan. "But, say—whenever this little old town does loosen up and get friendly it goes the limit. Say you took a little stroll in the park, Miss Conway—don't you think it might chase away some of your mullygrubs? And if you'd allow me—"

"Thanks, Mr. Donovan. I'd be pleased to accept of your escort if you think the company of one whose heart is filled with gloom could be anyways agreeable to you."

Through the open gates of the iron-railed, old, downtown park, where the elect once took the air, they strolled and found a quiet bench.

There is this difference between the grief of youth

and that of old age: youth's burden is lightened by as much of it as another shares; old age may give and give, but the sorrow remains the same.

"He was my fiancé," confided Miss Conway, at the end of an hour. "We were going to be married next spring. I don't want you to think that I am stringing you, Mr. Donovan, but he was a real Count. He had an estate and a castle in Italy. Count Fernando Mazzini was his name. I never saw the beat of him for elegance. Papa objected, of course, and once we eloped, but papa overtook us, and took us back. I thought sure papa and Fernando would fight a duel. Papa has a livery business—in P'kipsee, you know.

"Finally, papa came around all right, and said we might be married next spring. Fernando showed him proofs of his title and wealth, and then went over to Italy to get the castle fixed up for us. Papa's very proud, and when Fernando wanted to give me several thousand dollars for my trousseau he called him down something awful. He wouldn't even let me take a ring or any presents from him. And when Fernando sailed I came to the city and got a position as cashier in a candy store.

"Three days ago I got a letter from Italy, forwarded from P'kipsee, saying that Fernando had been killed in a gondola accident.

"That is why I am in mourning. My heart, Mr. Donovan, will remain forever in his grave. I guess I am poor company, Mr. Donovan, but I can not take any interest in no one. I should not care to keep you from gaiety and your friends who can smile and entertain you. Perhaps you would prefer to walk back to the house?"

Now, girls, if you want to observe a young man hustle out after a pick and shovel, just tell him that your heart is in some other fellow's grave. Young men are grave-robbers by nature. Ask any widow. Something must be done to restore that missing organ to weeping girls in *crêpe de Chine*. Dead men certainly got the worst of it from all sides.

"I'm awful sorry," said Mr. Donovan gently. "No, we won't walk back to the house just yet. And don't say you haven't no friends in this city, Miss Conway. I'm awful sorry, and I want you to believe I'm your friend, and that I'm awful sorry."

"I've got his picture here in my locket," said Miss Conway, after wiping her eyes with her handkerchief. "I never showed it to anybody, but I will to you, Mr. Donovan, because I believe you to be a true friend."

Mr. Donovan gazed long and with much interest at the photograph in the locket that Miss Conway opened for him. The face of Count Mazzini was one to command interest. It was a smooth, intelligent, bright, almost a handsome face—the face of a strong, cheerful man who might well be a leader among his fellows.

"I have a larger one, framed, in my room," said Miss Conway. "When we return I will show you that. They are all I have to remind me of Fernando. But he ever will be present in my heart, that's a sure thing."

A subtle task confronted Mr. Donovan—that of supplanting the unfortunate Count in the heart of Miss Conway. This his admiration for her determined him to do. But the magnitude of the undertaking did not seem to weigh upon his spirits. The sympathetic but cheerful friend was the rôle he essayed, and he played it so successfully that the next half-hour found them conversing pensively across two plates of ice-cream, though yet there was no diminution of the sadness in Miss Conway's large gray eyes.

Before they parted in the hall that evening she ran upstairs and brought down the framed photograph wrapped lovingly in a white silk scarf. Mr. Donovan surveyed it with inscrutable eyes.

"He gave me this the night he left for Italy," said Miss Conway. "I had one for the locket made from this."

"A fine-looking man," said Mr. Donovan heartily. "How would it suit you, Miss Conway, to give me pleasure of your company to Coney next Sunday afternoon?"

A month later they announced their engagement to Mrs. Scott and the other boarders. Miss Conway continued to wear black.

A week after the announcement the two sat on the same bench in the downtown park, while the fluttering leaves of the trees made a dim kinetoscopic picture of them in the moonlight. But Donovan had worn a look of abstracted gloom all day. He was so silent to-night that love's lips could not keep back any longer the questions that love's heart propounded.

"What's the matter, Andy, you are so solemn and grouchy to-night?"

"Nothing, Maggie."

"I know better. Can't I tell? You never acted this way before. What is it?"

"It's nothing much, Maggie."

"Yes it is, and I want to know. I'll bet it's some other girl you are thinking about. All right. Why don't you go and get her if you want her? Take your arm away, if you please."

"I'll tell you then," said Andy wisely; "but I guess you won't understand it exactly. You've heard of Mike Sullivan, haven't you? 'Big Mike' Sullivan, everybody calls him."

"No, I haven't," said Maggie. "And I don't want to, if he makes you act like this. Who is he?"

"He's the biggest man in New York," said Andy, almost reverently. "He can do about anything he wants to with Tammany or any other old thing in the political line. He's a mile high and as broad as East River. You say anything against Big Mike and you'll have a million men on your collarbone in about two seconds. Why, he made a visit over to the old country awhile back, and the kings took to their holes like rabbits.

"Well, Big Mike's a friend of mine. I ain't more than deuce-high in the district as far as influence goes, but Mike's as good a friend to a little man, or a poor man, as he is to a big one. I met him to-day on the Bowery, and what do you think he does? Comes up and shakes hands. 'Andy,' says he, 'I've been keeping cases on you. You've been putting in some good licks over on your side of the street, and I'm proud of you. What'll you take to drink?' He takes a cigar, and I take a highball. I told him I was going to get married in two weeks. 'Andy,' says he, 'send me an invitation, so I'll keep in mind of it, and I'll come to the wedding.' That's what Big Mike says to me; and he always does what he says.

"You don't understand it, Maggie, but I'd have one of my hands cut off to have Big Mike Sullivan at our wedding. It would be the proudest day of my life. When he goes to a man's wedding there's a guy being married that's made for life. Now, that's why I've maybe looking sore to-night."

"Why don't you invite him, then, if he's so much to the mustard?" said Maggie lightly.

"There's a reason why I can't," said Andy sadly. "There's a reason why he mustn't be there. Don't ask me what it is, for I can't tell you."

"Oh, I don't care," said Maggie. "It's something about politics, of course. But it's no reason why you can't smile at me."

"Maggie," said Andy presently, "do you think as much of me as you did of your—as you did of the Count Mazzini?"

He waited a long time, but Maggie did not reply. And then, suddenly she leaned against his shoulder and began to cry—to cry and shake with sobs, holding his arm tightly and wetting the *crêpe de Chine* with tears.

"There, there, there!" soothed Andy, putting aside his own trouble. "And what is it now?"

"Andy," sobbed Maggie, "I've lied to you and you'll never marry me, or love me any more. But I feel that I've got to tell. Andy, there never was so much as the little finger of a count. I never had a beau in my life. But all the other girls had, and they talked about 'em, and that seemed to make the fellows like 'em more. And, Andy, I look swell in black—you know I do. So I went out to a photograph store and bought that picture, and had a little one made for my locket, and made up all that story about the Count and about his being killed, so I could wear black. And nobody can love a liar and you'll shake me, Andy, and I'll die for shame. Oh, there never was anybody I liked but you—and that's all."

But instead of being pushed away she found Andy's arm folding her closely. She looked up and saw his face cleared and smiling.

"Could you—could you forgive me, Andy?"

"Sure," said Andy. "It's all right about that. Back to the cemetery for the Count. You've straightened everything out, Maggie. I was in hopes you would before the wedding-day. Bully girl!"

"Andy," said Maggie with a somewhat shy smile, after she had been thoroughly assured of forgiveness, "did you believe all that story about the Count?"

"Well, not to any large extent," said Andy, reaching for his cigar-case; "because it's Big Mike Sullivan's picture you've got in that locket of yours."

ALEXANDER

BY BEN BLOW

ALEXANDER

BY BEN BLOW

ALEXANDER sat out in the road, deserted, whooping in desolation, as he watched a crowd of barefoot urchins trudge down the distance in a haze of dust. His ears, low drooped, pictured the misery that possessed him, and every one in hearing distance knew that he was torn with sorrow. With agonized thumpings of his tail he beat up the dust behind him in tiny spurts, and when the boys turned noisily into a little by-lane—one of them lingering a moment to cast back an imaginary rock of ponderous weight—he gave himself anew to desolation and threw yet more pathos into the whoops that already wrenched his overburdened soul.

"If he ain't the durndest fool I ever seen," observed the urchin who had devoted a brief moment of his valuable time to delivering a farewell threat, "he's clost kin. He kin chaw off more trouble an' howl over it louder than any pup I ever had, an' that ain't been no few. Pap says he kind o' thinks, sometimes, that the pup wuz born noodle-headed an' it keeps gettin' worse, hey?"

The inquiry was addressed to a freckle-faced youngster who lacked two upper front teeth.

"Yep," was the reply. "You called the turn, Fatty. That ain't no lie."

"You bet it ain't no lie," said Fatty. "S'pose we took him 'n' what then? While we're a-scrapin' our pants buttons off belly-whackin' up to where the melons is, nine chances to one he's goin' to skyte out an' whoop aroun' till every guinea on the place squalls, 'Water-melon-patch, water-melon-patch,' an' then—"

Johnny Simmons cut in glibly, "An' then that blame waggle-legged hired man o' old Harkinses'll come a-runnin' out an' shoot us full o' salt."

Meantime, while his former friends were congratulating themselves on his absence, Alexander still sat out in the road bewailing his blighted life. Hoarse from much vocalizing, he emitted the long-drawn, excruciating whoops with which he was accustomed to reproach the moon for being full. His eyes half closed in ecstasy of misery, his ears filled with melodious outpourings from his harassed soul, he was absorbed, and did not notice an approaching vehicle until the soft thudding of horses' feet drew very close, and then, turning a mournful face over his shoulder, he was galvanized into frenzied terror, and departed down the road in vast, spraddle-legged leaps. The glance had shown him Deacon Simmons in his buggy, coming home from Warsaw, while close at hand, with evil in his eyes, his neck scruffed up, was Deacon Simmons's Boze, Boze the redoubtable, Boze who had licked every dog in Macedon.

Terror lent wings to Alexander's somewhat gawky paws. The dust he kicked up made him resemble a whizzing comet, leading a nebulous yellow tail. His wails ceased. He needed all his breath for purposes of locomotion. He fled silently, with fear palpitating in his heart. Reaching the lane, he bolted madly in, gathering yet more speed from hope that sprung anew. Close behind he heard deep breathing, and the snick of awful jaws that snapped in lustful hungering for his blood.

Around the corner swept Boze, almost nipping the frantic pup on the turn; then, knowing that Deacon Simmons would not go that way, he slowed up, stopped, and sneezed away the dust that had settled on him from the cloud stirred up by Alexander. And then he laughed. His tongue hung out, his ribs heaved. Far up the lane he saw the pup, his legs spread in wide disorder, departing at a rate of speed that would have made a jack-rabbit envious. Boze straightened up, kicked out his hind legs, scratching up and casting far behind him little bits of turf, looked longingly again at his escaped prey, and said, "Woof! Woof-woof!" with great contempt.

"'Most got him that time, didn't you, old boy?" said Deacon Simmons, coming up. His face was humorous, and his tone caressing, for he knew that a thorough rolling in the dust was all that Alexander had escaped. Then, smiling happily, he drove on home, in blissful ignorance that close at hand, hid in a concealing elderberry thicket, was his son and heir, ringleader of a predatory band whose mouths watered and whose stomachs ached with hungering for the melons of his friend and neighbor, Peter Harkins, and that Alexander, in his flight, had traced their footsteps up the lane.

Beset behind, abandoned by his friends before, nothing was left for Alexander but to howl some more. Seating himself, he glanced around, settled into comfort, pointed his nose skyward, and tuned again a wail of desolation from his dusty vocal chords. "Ur-roo, ur-roo, ar-roo!" A rock, dropped from the clear sky, lit between his paws, raising a puff of dust, and bounded against his stomach, drum-taut to give a better volume to his voice. The howl terminated in a frightened "Oof!" as his muscles, contracting involuntarily, catapulted him straight up until he cleared the ground. His ears, soaring under the impetus of his sudden leap, flapped skyward, setting off his frightened face, while with wild paws he clawed desperately at the intangible air. From the deep of the elderberry thicket, across the fence, the boys emerged. Checked in his impulse for flight by the memory of Boze, the pup assumed a mournfully apologetic air, and wagged his tail.

"Dog rat his skin, d'you ever see sech a pup?" asked Fatty, with undisguised disgust. "'S a lucky thing we seen your daddy comin' in time to duck into the elderberries, hey?"

This remark was directed to Johnny Simmons, who gave it unqualified assent, and then observed, "Ought to 'a' tied him in the first place."

"That's what," said Fatty, blazing into wrath. "I've a durn good notion to climb over the fence an' lambast the stuffin' out o' him, right now. Did your durndest to git us noticed, didn't yuh!" He was speaking now to Alexander, who settled meekly into the dust and wagged a sad, apologetic tail. Johnny Simmons, with meditative mien, bent a stout elderberry, and when it popped, breaking, the pup cowered yet lower, shivered a trifle, bethought himself of flight, and then remembered again that back of him was Boze, Boze the relentless, who even now might be sneaking on him unaware. He cast a hasty look around, then dropped his lean head to his dust-smeared paws, and hopelessly resigned himself to torture with appealing, mournful eyes.

"Beatin' don't do no good," said Fatty, softened at this sight of utter wo. "He'd howl so everybody in a mile an' a half'd think we wuz prying his back teeth out with a rat-tail file, an' he wouldn't go home; naw, you c'd beat him into pulp, an' all he'd do'd be to waller an' howl. We got to take him, that's all they is to it. We jist got to, that's all."

Then there arose before Alexander's apprehensive eyes a champion in the person of "Whitey Wilkins," a tow-headed youngster whose blue overalls, supported by a single gallus, hung farther down one leg than the other, making him seem to limp as he walked. "Aw, don't beat him, Johnny," he begged, "aw, don't. How'd you like to be left behind if you wuz the pup? I'll take care o' him, honest injun, if some o' you fellers'll lift me a melon."

"I'll git you a melon, Whitey," Johnny Simmons responded promptly, much relieved, "but you got to swing on to the pup awful tight."

Sliding his hand far into the depths of the half-masted pants leg, Whitey Wilkins produced with great triumph a length of grimy twine, hid in some moment of boyish inspiration for just such need. "Here's a piece o' bull cord," he said; "I guess he ain't a-goin' to bust that. Hyah, Sandy, hyah, Sandy, hyah, puppy, come here, you durn fool."

One hand patted the front of one blue leg in irresistible invitation, while the other held in readiness the tether that was to bind. Alexander arose, reassured by Whitey's advances, and squirmed between two lower rails of the snake fence. Humbly crawling, he sought his champion, and with hot tongue licked his dusty, brier-scratched bare feet. A kindly little hand patted the pup's muzzle, then closed firmly on one ear, while the other hand emerged from concealment, bearing the bull cord, and Alexander was tied, tied so securely that a fringe of hair stood up around his neck like a spiked collar. The crowd resumed its march toward the melons, with Whitey Wilkins, dragging Alexander, bringing up the rear.

Across a field, over a rail fence, through which Alexander was forced with protesting howls, into another field and down to a creek, the march led.

"Now, fellers," said Johnny Simmons, "we foller up the creek till we git to a gully, then we take the gully an' that lands us in ol' Harkinses patch, but we got to do some awful snaky crawlin', cuz the grass ain't high an' they's no tellin' but what that blame hired man o' old Harkinses is settin' up right now a-layin' fur us, with his eyes peeled on them melons."

With a view to future depredations, Johnny Simmons had marked out the ground long before, and, led by him, the boys trudged up the creek, Alexander joyful even in restraint. When they reached the gully they stopped and gathered close, and Johnny Simmons spoke again.

"Say, Fatty," he said, "better leave the pup an' Whitey here. We don't want Sandy no closter, cuz he might snake his head loose, hey?"

"How fur is it?" inquired Whitey, not the least abashed at being mentioned second to the pup.

"Right smart piece up the gully, Whitey," was the

answer. "You better stay here. No tellin' what's goin' to happen when you go melon hookin'. If that blame hired man happens to skyte out after us you don' need to lose no sleep. Just turn the pup loost an' make out you're crawfishin'. You ain't had no hand in melon hookin', no, you ain't. You just happened to pick this place cuz it's a likely lookin' spot fur crawfish. Crawfishin' ain't no crime, is it?"

"One spot's good as another spot," responded Whitey. "All the same to me. I'm the kind that changes spots when I git tired. Don't you lose no sleep over me, but don't you git excited an' furgit to lift me a melon, cuz I ain't anxious to go back an' lift one all alone!"

" 'Nough said," answered Johnny Simmons. "You git one if any one does. Come on, fellers, snooks while we're in the gully, belly-whacks to the ground when we git to the patch; le's go!" Stooping, they went up the gully, disappearing around a little bend, and Alexander and his guardian were alone. The pup whimpered, looking after them, and when they had disappeared from view, looked craftily at Whitey; then, without warning, made a frantic leap, hoping to free himself. Off guard and utterly surprised, Whitey grabbed wildly, his bare foot slipped, and plunging heavily, he fell upon the pup, squeezing out a howl. Swiftly he clapped a muddy hand over Alexander's muzzle, and then flaming with righteous wrath, he belted him upon a mud-bespattered ear.

"Durn your picture!" he gasped. "Don't you know who your friend is? Here I'm a-missin' all the fun fur you an' you go actin' scratch. Mind, now, or you'll see what I do to you."

He got up, releasing Alexander's muzzle cautiously. The pup regained his feet and shook himself, beginning at his ears and ending at the very tip of his mud-smeared tail, liberally bespattering his guardian with ooze, and then glanced upward with one humorous eye, entirely unabashed. The boy seated himself on a tuft of swamp grass and the pup, snuggling close to him, rested his head on his knee and looked up into his face with honest eyes. A muddy hand stole out and gently patted the nestling head, and with perfect confidence that his words were understood the boy spoke.

"What in time makes you sech a fool, Sandy?" he asked. "You don't do nothin' but waller in trouble from mornin' till night. I lay right now you're up to some devilment."

The pup wagged his tail, while his soft brown eyes denied utterly that he harbored any thought of evil, and the boy patted his head again. Far up the creek a cow came down to drink. A bullfrog close at hand dived head first into the cool waters with a "plop." The pug wriggled—his quick eye saw the cow, his quick ear heard the frog; he wanted to bark, longed to bark, started to bark, when a hand clamped his jaws close and a second grimy, hard little hand dealt him another cuff on the ear.

"They ain't no trustin' you," said the boy. *"Durn* you! Blame me if I don't git mad at you yit. I ain't a-goin' to fool with you much longer." He raised the pup's head and looked down deep into his eyes. "Y' hear?" he said. "Y' better mind."

The pup wagged his tail. The cow departed, her thirst slaked, and the bullfrog lifted his round, knobby eyes, which looked like tiny bubbles, above the water and viewed his natural enemies with unconcealed distrust. A catbird coming down to bathe perched close by with flirting tail, miauing at the boy, whose arm ached with desire to get up and paste a rock at her. The low-hung, fleecy clouds, swept wind-blown before the sun, made shadows that raced across the fields like cavalry in charge. The pup wriggled again, but the boy clung close to the string.

The pup wriggled yet more, looking up the gully. The boy followed suit and saw a sight of gladness: Five hot urchins, one struggling manfully under two huge, striped melons, the others each with one as striped and as huge, came into view, and Fatty, speaking thickly, replied to an inquiring look:

"Naw, we didn't git 'em, naw."

"Come on, fellers," said Johnny Simmons, not made the least bit reckless by success. "Le's git. Never lay clost to trouble when you kin move. Say you, Fatty! Tie that string o' Sandy's to a pants button an' let Whitey tote his melon. I ain't got no arms left."

Fatty, obedient, set his melon down, and turning partially around within his clothes, tethered the frisking pup to a button far in the rear. Then Whitey Wilkins picked up his melon and Fatty Peters picked up his, and the crowd moved on to safety and the feast. When they had reached the spring that marked the ending of their pilgrimage they put the melons in and piled cool leaves and clinging mud upon them, released the pup from bondage and sat down to rest. And then the youngest member of the crowd, a black-eyed urchin whose dark hair thatched a head of vast philosophy, made this profound remark:

"Say, fellers, ain't it just nifty to be a kid?"

"Oh, I do' know," said Johnny Simmons. "Goin' to school ain't no picnic, but it's got to be done. I never thought chores was much fun, neither. Fur a good time in this world kind o' seems to me I'd rather be a dog. Look at Sandy. Does he have to scrabble fur a livin'? Does he have to worry his brains over spellin'? Ain't a place to sleep give him? An' when he grows up he ain't never goin' to have nothin' to do but snooze in the sun an' git up now 'n' then an' chase a shoat out o' the yard. D'you s'pose fur a minute it tastes bad to him when he's a-chawin' a hog's ear? Not him; he likes it, he does."

"Dogs can't talk, though," said Billy Day, defending the niftiness of kidhood. "Kind o' seems to me I'd miss that."

"Naw, they can't talk, but they kin wag their tails mighty knowin'. Anyway, how d'you know they can't talk. My daddy says Doc Henderson told him that them big-bug men in Wash'nt'n told him that even the teeny little ants talk to each other. Now what you got to say?"

This inquiry was made triumphantly, as if definitely settling the discussion, but Fatty arose in negation that was contemptuously serene.

"Ah, g'wan," he said. "Kin they hear what the ants say? G'wan."

"Animals is got sense, though, 'n' I wouldn't be s'prised none if they could talk," interjected Whitey Wilkins. "Our ol' Maje got bit by a cott'nmouth onct, an' pap says here's most likely where we have to raise another fool pup, but does he die? Naw, he don't die. What does he do? He hunts up a hog waller before the pizen gits to workin' good, an' buries hissef till they ain't nothin' but his nose sticks out an' he cures hissef. How'd he know mud'd cure? Has he even been snake-bit before? Naw, 'course he ain't, so some dog friend o' hisn that had must of told him 'bout the mud. Now is they any answer to that? Kin they talk or can't they?"

The discussion of old Maje's snake-bite experience was conducted with much asperity while the boys absorbed the watermelons, now lusciously chill, and Alexander, tired of bombardment with melon seed, wandered away into the woods. Fatty Peters maintained the negative with wise logic between vast mouthfuls of sweet pulp.

"How'd the first dog find out mud'd cure?" he demanded. "He didn't have no time to git advice. Somethin' had to be done an' done durn quick. I tell you 'twasn't nothin' but instinc'. Some o' you fellers tell me what makes a dog put all four feet clost together an' turn round three times 'fore he lays down. D'you ever see a cat do that-a-way? Maybe you did, but I say you didn't, cuz cats don't do it."

Evidently regarding the argument as too strenuous for the occasion, Johnny Simmons created a diversion. "Where's that blame pup?" he asked.

As if in response to the inquiry Alexander spoke for himself. "Woof!" he said; "woof-woof!" Evidently he was far off, for the sound came faintly.

"I hear him," said Billy Day. "Maybe he's got somethin'; le's see!"

"Maybe," admitted Fatty, "an' maybe not. Y' never kin tell. Sometimes he gnaws holes in a brush pile till you'd think they wuz a fambly meetin' o' swamp rabbits bein' held there 'n' nothin' comes out; then again he'll let you kick a rabbit up between his paws an' not say nothin' till he's got a safe head start, 'n' then he takes out after him hollerin' bloody murder every jump."

" 'Tain't goin' to cost nothin' to see, though," said Johnny Simmons. "Come on, fellers; le's take a chanst."

The crowd arose and traced the sound of Alexander's frantic yelps. There he was, dancing before a brush pile, attacking it furiously with his teeth, now and then pulling the brush aside from an aperture that led into the depths and growling with deep rumblings between barks.

"I bet you he *is* got somethin'," said Billy Day. "Look at 'im. Sic, puppy; git 'im, boy!"

Alexander, enheartened, redoubled his efforts and his growls. Poking his lean head into the hole, he pushed and squirmed, humping his back up and shoving frantically with his hind legs, while with teeth and fore paws he strove to enlarge the opening. Gradually he went in, while the boys, drawing encouragement from his evident sincerity, poked into the brush pile and jumped on it, cheering him on the while with frenzied whoops. Burrowing desperately, the pup bored in and disappeared from view save for a tail that quivered with excitement, and from the depths came fierce snarling and relentless growls.

"Whoopee! Sic 'im, boy! Sick 'im, pup!" yelled Fatty, becoming excited. "Say, fellers, honest, he might 'a' holed a mink."

The wild chorus encouraging the pup to "sic 'im" rose noisily, the growls became more fierce, and then, in the unseen depths, there was an earthquake, followed by a wail of utterly heart-broken misery and despair. Uncertain as to the exact nature of the quarry, the boys withdrew as the agonized yelps sounded louder and yet more loud, and then the pup burst from the brush pile tail first, enveloped in an atmosphere that language is inadequate to picture or describe.

"Gee, fellers," said Fatty, "it's a polecat! Y' better run, cuz if it gits on you it ain't ever goin' to come off."

The crowd needed no further invitation to withdraw, while Alexander, blinded, wallowed in the dust, howling as if his heart would break, rubbing his nose, his eyes, anguished beyond the power of any sound to tell.

"That's him," gasped Fatty at a distance. "Oh, no, he ain't no fool. Oh, no, he don't hunt trouble any. Will he know a polecat nex' time, will he? Some o' you fellers hurry up an' tell me, will he, hey?"

There was no answer to this frantic appeal for information; they were all too full to laugh. But Alexander, by dint of much rubbing, had got one eye into condition to locate his companions, and with a deep yearning for comfort he made for Fatty, howling as he came.

"G'way!" yelled Fatty. "G'way, blame you!"

Alexander still came on and Fatty, stopping swiftly, caught up a club and landed it with deadly aim upon his heaving ribs, still shrieking frantically, "G'way! G'home!"

Staggered, the pup saw Johnny Simmons and made for him. A well-aimed missile tangled his legs and brought him to the ground, where he pawed wildly and raised a whoop of anguish greater than before. Then he saw Whitey Wilkins and set sail for him. Whitey fled, accompanied by much advice.

"Run, Whitey, run!" howled Fatty. "Don't let him git any on you. Run! Run!"

"Git a club an' belt 'im!" screamed Johnny, while Billy Day, believing firmly that his turn would come next, wrapped his stubby legs around a sapling and shinned up, rubbing his watermelon-laden stomach wofully indeed. In desperation Whitey, fleeing, seized a club and belted Alexander once again.

With his last hope gone, the last thump still hurting his suffering ribs, the dreadful smell still in his nose, the dreadful smart still burning in his eyes, Alexander stopped, cast a wild look around him, pointed his nose skyward, delivered one parting wail of despair and set off homeward, his tail frozen to his stomach, each frantic jump punctuated with a frantic howl. There was a riot of smell in the woods. There was a riot of howling that faded away swiftly, and then the boys lay down and rolled and yelled in an ecstasy, which was interrupted by Billy Day's falling out of his sapling in the effort to climb down. Finding that he wasn't hurt appreciably, the crowd slid back into convulsions of enjoyment until Billy, sobered by his tumble, holding his stomach affectionately, said: "Gee, fellers, we better git; maybe it'll stick to our clothes!"

Too much overcome to arise alone, Fatty was assisted into an upright position, and then the crowd departed with Billy still embracing his injured stomach, which, he asserted, was more painful when it joggled. Now and then a wild laugh swelled up and set a hysterical example that was contagious, and at length Fatty, gasping, managed to speak.

"Oh, no!" he said. "He ain't no fool, is he? D'you see him waller an' waller an' scratch an' root, tryin' to wipe off the smell?"

Peals of laughter greeted the words. The woods rang as the noisy troop set off homeward under the low-swung, western sun, which threw slanting, stripy shadows through the trees.

Alexander went homeward as the crow flies; went home to Macedon, because he knew no other place to go. He had no time to pick paths, he had no wish to loiter, he had no definite purpose. All he desired was to forget—to forget himself, to forget everything, to be annihilated, blotted out. Accompanied by a tumult of howlings, enveloped in a halo of vivid smell, he tore wildly on, his voice merely suggesting the misery that he tried to express. His vocabulary was too limited by far, but, striving nobly, he did his very best to tell the world the horror that was curdling his soul, and as he swept out into the big road he added to his accompaniments a cloud of dust that almost hid him as he flew. Past Whitey Wilkins's, stirring up Nip, the Wilkins's Irish terrier, into wild but hopeless chase, he sped. Chickens flew squawking away before him, and if dogs do communicate orally, then the entire canine population of Macedon knew that some vastness of grief, some unspeakable wo unknown to all previous experience, had overtaken one of them, as Alexander, shrieking, haled by the seven devils of despair, went home.

Mr. Peters, in the barnyard, heard him coming and turned in time to see him flash like a thunderbolt into the kitchen. There was a crash of crockery as he dived under the table, and Mrs. Peters, hardly recognizing the pup, lifted both floury hands appealingly and ejaculated:

"For the lan's sake!"

Then nerved to act, and act quickly, by the atmosphere that Alexander had brought with him, she grasped the broom and said, "Scat, you!" accompanying the exclamation with a hearty thump.

Alexander scatted. Out from the door he flashed like an arrow flitting from the bow of Robin Hood. Mr. Peters, stooping quickly, seized a chunk of stove wood, and as Alexander flew toward the spot that was sanctuary in his time of deepest trouble, heaved it at him and missed him by a fraction of an inch. As a flat stone drops edgeways into a still pool, Alexander dived head first into a hole under the barn.

"Jeemses rivers!" exclaimed Mr. Peters. "What next? Blamed if I ever did see such a fool in all my life."

A smile spread over his face, widened into a great grin, and as a mournful wail came out from underneath the barn he doubled up and laughed. Mrs. Peters came to the kitchen door. "Father," she said, "ain't you ashamed of yourself, acting that way? You cut up like a big boy."

Mr. Peters raised an appealing hand. "Don't, Elvira," he said imploringly; "don't scold me. It's so durn funny, his tryin' to run away from hisself." Another snuffling wail came from under the barn and a lean nose appeared seeking fresh air.

"Jeemses rivers," said Mr. Peters, "that pup certainly is loaded down with the troubles that he's discovered. Look at 'im, Elvira; ain't he full o' grief?" Then the humor of it struck Mrs. Peters and she sat down on the kitchen steps and laughed until the tears streamed down her cheeks.

Fatty got home hungry, with a faint suggestion of the smell that Alexander had brought clinging to his clothes. Stopping on the back porch long enough to dab his nose and cheeks with water, he added a polish from the roller towel and emptied the wash-basin upon the family cat, which departed shaking its paws in absolute disgust.

"Hello, mom!" he said. "Gee, I ain't nothin' but hungry. I c'd eat a keg o' nails."

"I expect you could," said Mrs. Peters smiling. "I expect you could. Have you washed?" With one hand she elevated his chin. "Your face is clean," she said, seeing traces of his recent ablutions.

"Yep," said Fatty. "Mom, we just had the dandiest time huntin'." Then he sniffed suspiciously. "Kind o' seems to me I smell somethin'!"

"I guess you do," said his mother. "What in the world you boys'll do to Sandy next is beyond me."

"We never done nothin' to him, mom," said Fatty, in earnest negation. "He didn't even stay with us long."

Mr. Peters appeared in time to catch the last remark. "No," he said, "no. Of course he didn't. Jeemses rivers, I c'd hear him comin' half a mile!"

Fatty laughed. "Say, pop," he said, "seems to me that pup must have some greyhound in him, cuz the last we seen o' him was a yaller streak. He wuzn't a-runnin'; he wuz a-flyin'. Gee, but he was a-burnin' up the dust."

Mrs. Peters smiled indulgently. "Come on," she said; "supper's ready. Sit down while everything's nice."

Everything was nice. Great heaps of bread, thickly spread, faded away before Fatty's onslaught. The unskimmed milk, cool from the spring house, was rich and satisfying, and hot gingerbread and peach preserves brought on the peace that comes when healthy, boyish hunger is appeased. Fatty was happy. His eyes drooped. Sleep stole upon him until at length he arose and departed, staggering, to bed; soon silence settled down on Macedon and everything was peace.

Under the barn, wide-eyed and sleepless, Alexander moaned. Perched high, the guineas smelt him and clucked little notes of fluttering alarm. The moon came up, shedding a mellow light and stilling the cicada's drone. A stripy yellow moonbeam wandered into Fatty's room and rested on his face. He turned himself, flung one bare arm above his head, still wrapped in dreams, and took a happy, deep-drawn breath that ended in a sigh of great content. His long, dark lashes swept his round, tanned cheek, and his lips, smile-wreathed, expressed that beatitude of rest known only to happy, tired and healthy boys. In the thrall of primal instinct, under the barn, the pup arose, turned thrice around and settled down again, and then he, Alexander, worn out, himself found sleep and followed Fatty into the land of dreamless peace.